The Royal College
of Physicians
and its Collections

The Royal College of Physicians and its Collections

An Illustrated History

Edited by Geoffrey Davenport,
Ian McDonald and Caroline Moss-Gibbons

THE ROYAL COLLEGE
OF PHYSICIANS

JAMES
X
JAMES

Picture Acknowledgements

The Advertising Archives 59; The National Portrait Gallery 134 (both margin pictures).

New photography by Geremy Butler
New architectural photography by Matthew Weinreb

ISBN 0 907 383 831

First published in 2001
© The Royal College of Physicians 2001

Project Editor and Designer: Susannah McSkimming
Printed and bound by G. Canale & C., Italy

Published by James & James (Publishers) Ltd
Gordon House Business Centre
6 Lissenden Gardens
London NW5 1LX

Half-title page illustration: 'The Reward of Cruelty' by William Hogarth.
Title page illustration: The Royal College of Physicians in Regent's Park.

Foreword

I am delighted to introduce this volume which has been a long-term dream of mine. The College is filled with treasures which are integral to the development and history of the College. The present volume leads the reader gently and beautifully through our long history. I hope everyone will derive as much pleasure and knowledge from it as I shall.

Kgnn Albert

Professor Sir George Alberti
President of the Royal College of Physicians

Preface

The Royal College of Physicians of London was founded in 1518 by a charter granted by King Henry VIII. Its fundamental aim then, as now, is well expressed in the words of the 1999/2003 strategic plan: 'promoting the highest standards of medical practice in order to improve health and health care'.

The founder of the College, Thomas Linacre, and later William Harvey were insistent on the importance in the College of providing facilities for physicians to continue to acquire knowledge and increase their depth of understanding not only in medicine, but in learning generally. In the centuries before the existence of public libraries and the founding of universities in London, the Library of the College was central to this role. After it was destroyed in the Great Fire of London of 1666, an honorary Fellow, the Marquis of Dorchester, responded by making it known that after his time, his own library (one of the finest in private hands in Europe) would come to the College. This it finally did in 1688. It covered the whole of learning and included rare books and manuscripts not only in natural history and medicine, but in mathematics, philosophy, law, theology and the classics.

To these treasures others have been and are still added by individual Fellows and the College itself: books, manuscripts, archives, silver, gold, the insignia of office, portraits, and the College's homes. In this book we have aimed to provide an outline of the history of the College and its role in medicine and society by giving accounts of some of the themes with which it has been involved and of the contribution of some of its Fellows prominent in the profession and beyond. Most of the illustrations have come from our own collections and the story of the College is built round them. Readers who want more formal details will find them in the official history, the first two volumes of which by Sir George Clark and the third by Dr Alec Cooke, are still available from the College. The latest volume, by Lord Asa Briggs, covering the years 1948–1983 will appear in 2002.

I would like to thank the Fellows and friends of the College who contributed to this book, the core of which derives from the incomparable breadth and depth of knowledge of Geoffrey Davenport, formerly its Librarian. Grateful thanks are also extended to Olivia Timbs for her invaluable sub-editing. Working with Hamish MacGibbon and Susie McSkimming of James & James has been a delight.

Ian McDonald
Harveian Librarian

Contents

The author's name, where specified, applies to the section indicated.
All other sections are by Geoffrey Davenport, former Librarian, RCP.

1

Introduction

From the initial endeavours to regularise the practice of medicine in the city of London, Fellows of the Royal College of Physicians and its forerunners have been concerned with setting standards in medical practice. Over the past 500 years, these efforts have attracted great scholars, doctors, scientists and other benefactors to its foundation and with them have come objects and icons, treatises and instruments, all part of the glorious legacy of the College.

New and established Fellows and Members of the Royal College of Physicians may have some hazy idea of the range of portraits, books and other artefacts owned by the College. Few will have an opportunity or the time to grasp any details about the extraordinary and rich heritage of which they are the current custodians.

This book is an introduction to the collections, putting the contents in historical perspective and demonstrating the relevance of certain items to current practice. It is designed to give some insight into and flavour of the role played by particular individuals in maintaining the ideals of the College (with varying degrees of success). It explains why the caduceus and mace, for example, appear on ceremonial occasions; and how the library was established, developed and will continue to grow with the College in the future.

But this history will show, as well, that the College did not always grasp the opportunities it had to lead the broader medical establishment forward. There are a number of instances where the Fellows were so concerned about protecting their professionalism in a narrow way that they missed the big picture. They failed to capitalise on the influence they could have enjoyed, were seen to be reactionary when there were huge gains to be made by being radical, and for long periods the College seemed to make no progress.

It was not until the latter decades of the twentieth century that the Royal College of Physicians really grasped the initiative on all fronts and began to have a positive impact on government, the public, as well as the medical profession. Through co-operation rather than exclusion, through the dissemination of public health and other medical reports rather than concentration alone on academic matters, the College now has a unique role at the centre of medicine and health policy.

Henry VIII. After Hans Holbein, c.1600. The portrait is owned by the College.

9

The first attempts were made to establish a regulatory body for physicians nearly 600 years ago. Physicians in the early part of the fifteenth century recognised the benefits of organising themselves to control the practice of medicine – in rudimentary form taking on the roles of both the College and the General Medical Council.

In 1421 the king, Henry V, received a petition 'from the physicians' requesting that unqualified practitioners should not be allowed to practise. The petition was accepted in principle but it was clearly unrealistic because of the shortage of qualified physicians and lack of a policing mechanism. Nothing more seems to have come of this venture but two years later a more modest scheme was put forward. Physicians joined with the surgeons to petition the mayor and aldermen of the city of London to control the practice of medicine and surgery within the City, and even to provide free treatment for those in need.

This first 'Comminalte' (the term 'College' was not used) was properly constituted with officers, including a President, and no one was to practise physic, or work in the craft of surgery, in the City until assessed by appropriate College officers. Any physician whose patient had an illness likely to be fatal also had to consult the officers about suitable treatment. In its short life – for unknown reasons this arrangement only lasted about eighteen months – officers of the Comminalte investigated at least one patient's complaint concerning an unsuccessful surgical operation, finding in favour of the doctor, while binding the complainant to silence.

Throughout the rest of the century, monitoring of standards continued in a more informal way. Physicians worked closely with apothecaries who dispensed prescribed medicines and it was in the interests of both groups to ensure that these were of a high standard. In 1472, for example, two physicians, together with a number of apothecaries, were appointed to investigate a complaint made to the mayor of the city of London that barrels and pots of theriac (treacle) brought to London (probably from Venice and Genoa) were unwholesome. The complaint was upheld and the treacle was incinerated at three different locations within the City, as a warning to other would-be fraudsters.

The 1518 Charter.

It was not until the year 1511 that a further formal attempt was made to prevent unqualified practitioners working as doctors. An Act was passed limiting the practice of medicine and surgery within the City of London, and seven miles around it, to physicians and surgeons who had been licensed by the Bishop of London or the Dean of St Paul's, on the advice of four qualified physicians and surgeons. Beyond this limit, no one was to practise as a physician or surgeon without the approval of his local bishop. However, the body now known as the Royal College of Physicians of London was founded in 1518 with a charter granted by Henry VIII with no regard to this Act.

Both physicians and surgeons were licensed under the 1511 Act but the two groups took different regulatory routes. The barber-surgeons were more conventional for the time. They had been incorporated as a City company in 1462 giving members the right to practise surgery and they already had their own Hall and were firmly established in the City hierarchy as the Barber-Surgeons Company when the College was established. They gained a new royal charter in 1540. Throughout the fifteenth century the trades and professions in London, including the medically oriented ones like the spicers and grocers (to which the apothecaries belonged) had been obtaining royal charters and grants of incorporation. So by the early sixteenth century the university-trained physicians were something of an anomaly and one of the few groups without a corporate identity.

The initiative to petition Henry VIII for the foundation of a College came from Thomas Linacre [see also page 140] who was to be the first President. Linacre was a scholar with a high reputation, as well as a physician to the Court, and so was able to exert a great deal of influence on the king and his entourage. Linacre was inspired by the organisation of medicine he had encountered in Italy, particularly at the medical colleges at Venice and Padua. Like its Italian counterparts, the English College aimed to maintain high standards of patient care. In the words of the English translation of the Charter: 'to curb the audacity of those wicked men who shall profess medicine more for the sake of their avarice than from the assurance of any good conscience, whereby many inconveniences may ensue to the rude and credulous populace.'

Linacre and his co-founders wanted a royal and academic body rather than a trade guild, even though the College's principal activity initially was to control entry into the profession exactly like the livery companies. The College also aspired to be a national organisation, but the Charter limited its control of medical practice to the City of London and for a radius of seven miles around. The Act of Parliament of 1523 ratifying the Charter ended with a clause recommending that in the rest of England where there was insufficient expertise to examine any physicians wishing to practise, the College should be consulted, though this was treated more as a recommendation than a directive. To all intents and purposes any physician who submitted to be examined for the Extra-Licence (*extra urbem* – to practise only beyond the seven-mile radius) did so voluntarily and the College's power base was restricted to London.

Where the London College differed from the Venetian College was in not having such a close involvement with public health, although from early on it took some interest – if not always successfully. When plague threatened in 1625, for example, it advised the Lord Mayor on the precautions to be taken against the infection and its advice to the Privy Council in 1630 was issued officially, with further editions in 1636 and 1665. The College's role in public health issues was somewhat patchy over the following 400 years, until it made a notable contribution in the mid-twentieth century, with its role in establishing the health service and issuing the first warning of the dangers of tobacco smoking [see pages 56–9].

The 1518 Charter and confirmatory Act of 1523 between them specified as officers a President, eight Elects who chose him, four Censors to assist him in his duties and two counsellors to advise him [see page 155]. Other officers came later. It was John Caius, a Padua graduate like Linacre, and President from 1555 who regularised the College administration, recording its meetings, its prosecutions of empirics and inspections of apothecaries' drugs and introducing greater formality into proceedings [see pages 98–9, 103, 111].

The Seventeenth Century

In the early part of the seventeenth century life became harder for the College and in some respects it paid a high price for remaining inward-looking. It continued to protect the right of its own Fellows and Licentiates alone to practise medicine in London, but its authority was challenged with increasing frequency.

Many physicians with doctorates of medicine, particularly from the English universities, resented the College's right to re-examine them [see pages 28–9]. Degrees from foreign universities were clearly mistrusted as they could be so easily obtained by submitting a thesis after a short period of study. ('Foreign' initially embraced Scottish universities, although once the two Crowns were united in 1603 provision had to be made for all physicians to practise at the court of James I.) This restrictive policy was patently unfair as in the case of Gerard Boet who refused to acknowledge the College's jurisdiction. He was pursued relentlessly – from 1630 until he was finally admitted as a Licentiate in 1646 – despite having a medical doctorate from Leyden – just as good as its English equivalents.

As part of its ambition to control the practice of medicine completely the College supported a bid for independence made by the apothecaries from the Grocers' Company, then a considerable power in the City. The College may have hoped that this would make it easier to confine the apothecaries to the dispensing of drugs, but the plan backfired. When the apothecaries received their charter in December 1617 it gave the College much less control over their affairs than the Fellows might have wished.

The title page of the Pharmacopoeia Londinensis, *1618.*

For a start there were too few Fellows and Licentiates to provide all medical care that the city required and their services were too expensive for the majority of the population. The apothecaries recognised this and were united in their desire to be allowed to give advice when and where it was needed. Moreover, they were prepared to battle it out [see pages 28–33].

But the establishment of the Society of Apothecaries also coincided with the revival by the College of a pharmacopoeia – a standard listing of medicines and their composition. Following the abortive attempt of 1589–94 the first edition of the *Pharmacopoeia Londinensis* was published in 1618 under the aegis of the College. The apothecaries were instructed by royal declaration to make up medicines only according to the formulae specified in it and although there were inconsistencies in the first version, its existence was significant proof that the College was leading the way in standard-setting [see pages 48–53].

At about the same time, William Harvey conducted his research into the circulation of the blood. It has been suggested that this work was reported as part of his Lumleian lectures but it seems more likely that he conducted it privately. He made it clear, however, in the introduction to his book *De motu cordis* published in 1628 that he had demonstrated his experiments to some of the Fellows for their interest and opinion. And undoubtedly his brilliant experimental methods as well as his major discovery, once it had become accepted, reflected creditably on the College.

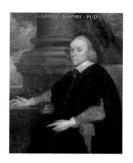

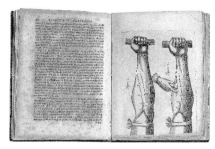

Top: *William Harvey.*
Above: *pages from his work* De motu cordis.

Harvey also provided a new library extension for the College at its premises at Amen Corner and was probably instrumental in getting the Marquis of Dorchester – the College's greatest benefactor – elected an Honorary Fellow.

After the Restoration in 1660, the use of the word 'Royal' was attached to the College's name with increasing frequency [see pages 26–8] even though (or perhaps because) it had not always reflected the political leanings of the Presidents and Fellows in the immediate past.

In other respects the 1660s was not a propitious decade. The Great Plague of 1665 and the Fire of London in 1666 were both disasters for the College. During the plague the abandoned College building was broken into and the silver stolen. The College's coffers that had just been boosted by the election in 1664 of 73 Honorary Fellows were emptied overnight, making it difficult to find the money for a new building after the old one was subsequently destroyed in the fire the following year. It was not built until 1674 and the anatomy theatre, added later with money from Sir John Cutler, was not ready for use until early 1679 [see page 64].

The first Harveian Librarian, Dr Christopher Merrett and the Bedell managed to save the caduceus, some valuable documents and a number of library books from the fire, but it is impossible to say how much else was lost. The subsequent dispute between the College and Merrett, who had been a great defender of the College's rights and privileges in print, is a matter for regret [see page 71].

During the reign of James II the old charter was superseded and brought further problems for the College. The new one named 80 Fellows, among them a number who would not have been elected according to the criteria in operation under the previous charter, and rejected others on the grounds that they were likely to be religious dissenters. Somehow, the College contrived to keep within the Fellowship all except the obvious Catholics who were unacceptable to William III's government.

The College's pamphlet on the subject of its dispensaries.

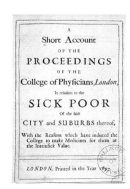

It was a messy compromise and not always to the College's advantage. Its next big adventure, the opening of the Dispensary in 1696, was bound up with the continuing rivalry with the apothecaries. There were now more Fellows in sympathy with the apothecaries' point of view – that there should be fewer restrictions placed on them – than there would have been in the smaller College.

The Eighteenth Century

Sir George Clark wrote in the second volume of the official College history published in 1966: 'Every long-lived institution must have its bad times. There is a *prima facie* case for thinking that the eighteenth century was one of the worst periods of the College of Physicians.'

Although the century was not a great one and ultimately the College had to succumb to sweeping reforms in the 1830s, for many decades all was quiet and little seemed to be happening. However, there was plenty of drama to make up for it, starting with the collapse of the Dispensary [see pages 30–3]. And in the 1760s the College's most serious and certainly most violent internal revolt took place when disgruntled Licentiates took matters into their own hands and attempted to demand a bigger role in the governance of the College [see pages 33–6].

As a result, the statutes were interpreted a little more liberally under the alternating presidencies of Sir George Baker and Thomas Gisborne, and the animosity between the Fellows and the Licentiates (who had by this time become much more numerous than the Fellows) gradually reduced in the last decades. Lord Mansfield had judged in 1771 that the distinction the College made between Fellows and Licentiates was not illegal, but advised it to beware of being too restrictive. In 1784 Dr Richard Warren proposed a new statute that gave the President the right to nominate Licentiates for promotion to the Fellowship. By the end of the century eight of them had been promoted this way, including three of the members of the Society of Collegiate Physicians. Several of these were Scottish graduates, so a few exceptions were beginning to be made to the strict division between the Oxbridge graduates and the others.

And there were some academic high spots in the century: the College's first journal, the *Medical Transactions* [see page 54] was launched in 1760, and in the 1745 and 1788 revisions of the *Pharmacopoeia* some semblance of rationality began to appear [see page 49].

'The Siege of Warwick Castle; or The Battle between the Fellows and Licentiates'. Artist unknown.

The Nineteenth Century

The College stuck fairly tenaciously to the two categories of Licentiates and Fellows until well into the nineteenth century – applying rigid rules when they were not always appropriate. At the beginning of the first decade when one John Clarke was discovered to have exceeded his licence to prescribe only in obstetric cases, the College's response was draconian – and similar to the response it had made in parallel cases over a century earlier.

A majority of Fellows refused his request to take the examination for the full Licence and they considered legal action against him. Only reluctantly did they accept the advice of the Attorney General, Sir Vicary Gibbs, that although under the terms of its constitution the College could prosecute, this would not be 'a favorable Case for instituting such an Action'. Moreover, discussion in a public court of what did or did not constitute a disorder connected with the obstetric art 'would be shocking, & should if possible be avoided'.

The presidency of Sir Lucas Pepys (1804–11), 'a blunt, good-natured and popular man who did not excel in tact' according to Sir George Clark, brought mixed fortunes for the College and a further period of battening down the hatches. It began with the abolition of the short-lived Licence in Midwifery. And when Edward Harrison, a Lincolnshire doctor, attempted from around 1807 onwards to promote medical regulation for all branches of the profession countrywide, the College opposed him on principle.

Sir Lucas Pepys (1742–1830), PRCP 1804–11. Pencil and watercolour by H. Edridge.

Fellows insisted not only on its existing rights but on an enlargement of the powers of the existing authorities to cover the provinces, despite its previous lack of interest in what went on outside London. But in 1808 it had to accept on legal advice that it could no longer prosecute under its own jurisdiction but only in the courts of law.

At the end of Pepys's first year the Censors had reiterated the College's right to control the practice of medicine in London, regretting the indulgence shown to those with licences from Oxford and Cambridge who had not yet obtained their degrees. They also feared for the loss of the College's rights through disuse, resolving to investigate those with mere Licences in Midwifery who practised medicine generally.

This reactionary position was a wasted opportunity and the surgeons and apothecaries were able to profit by the College's stance. The College could have been in the vanguard of reform and had influence over the practice of medicine all over the country if it had taken a different route.

A proposal put forward to Comitia in 1804 in a paper by John Latham, later to be President (1813–20), recommended that to qualify as a physician a Candidate had to have a degree from an English, Irish or Scottish university obtained after a full course of study. This would have overcome the College's objection to degrees from Aberdeen and St Andrew's that could still be obtained by recommendation. Suggestions were also made for minimum requirements for surgeons, apothecaries and druggists and the country was to be divided into districts, each with a physician to supervise licensing and registration. These were to be appointed by and from the Royal College, thus retaining their traditional control of entry to the profession. These proposals would have provided a complete system of examination and registration without offending the sensibilities of the old medical corporations.

In the event the way forward for ordinary town and country doctors came from pressure by the Association of Surgeon-Apothecaries which led to the Apothecaries Act of 1815. This created an examination in basic medicine, surgery, and later midwifery – the first British qualification covering the whole of medical practice – conducted by the Society of Apothecaries (the LSA).

The College was not happy. In 1843, after the reforms of the mid-1830s, when the Extra-Licentiate Edwin Lankester – already MRCS, LSA and MD Heidelberg and shortly to be elected FRS – moved to London, the College sent the Bedell to admonish him. He decided to take the examination for the full Licence in 1846 and failed the second (pathology) part, but carried on practising, blighting his chances of obtaining a post in a London voluntary hospital. This seems particularly short-sighted and protectionist as the mood was swinging ever more in favour of generalists and an increasing acceptance that surgeons and apothecaries could practise as 'general practitioners' (the term came into use in the 1830s and 1840s).

By this time the College's City location was no longer seen as prestigious. The London residences of the physicians' more notable patients were now located in the developing area further to the west. The College had been contemplating a move at least since the time of Sir Lucas Pepys's presidency and provided for it in 1814 by an Act of Parliament allowing it to move its headquarters to Westminster. But the grand opening of the Trafalgar Square building in 1825, with a large contingent of the aristocracy present [see page 65] did nothing to suggest that any radical change in thinking would come with the new building.

However, the College doors would not stay metaphorically closed indefinitely and change was on the way, although not without some pressure from the medical press and the 1834 House of Commons committee on medical education. The system of entry to the College by a postgraduate Membership examination and subsequent promotion to the Fellowship by recommendation began when the distinction between Fellows with their Oxbridge MDs and Licentiates (all others except for a privileged few) was ended by the reforms of 1835–6. This made the Licence the entry qualification to the College for all with at least five years' medical study and three years' hospital experience [see page 45].

The transmutation of this Licence into the Membership (MRCP) in 1859, available to all who applied, was little more than a change of name, although the Extra-Licentiates who had taken a much easier examination did well by their promotion to Member – they had not previously been eligible for the Fellowship. The examination continued to take the same form until 1867. The undergraduate Licence instituted in 1859, later to be joined with the MRCS England, had no previous exact parallel.

Sir Henry Halford. Stipple engraving by J. Cochran after Henry Room, 1838.

The 1835–6 reforms took place under the presidency of Sir Henry Halford, the great medical courtier and ironically generally thought an arch-conservative. But it is not unknown for radical reforms to be pushed through by a trusted conservative leader, when the same reforms would be rejected if their proponent were thought to be more visionary.

The 1830s were, of course, a great decade of reform. The Fellows must have been fully aware of the great Reform Act of 1832, the Factory Act of 1833, and the Municipal Reform Act that Parliament was discussing as they debated their own constitutional changes. They must also have registered the abolition of the Test and Corporation Acts in 1828 which removed restrictions

16

on the holding of public office by Protestant dissenters and the passing of the Catholic Emancipation Act in 1829.

Halford would appear to have been aware of what was needed. He had already applied more frequently than any previous President the modified 1784 bye-law giving him the right to propose Licentiates for the Fellowship. Richard Bright, for example, an Edinburgh graduate from a Bristol family [see pages 90–2] was elected by this means in 1832, the year following the publication of the second part of his *Reports on medical cases* – a publication that demonstrated to the wider world that he was highly talented. Halford was also under pressure from some junior Fellows to end the College's insistence on the classical education provided by Oxford and Cambridge and that the College 'should be open to all, no matter where or how educated, provided they came up to a standard of mere medical knowledge.' Halford's own essay 'On the education and conduct of a physician', read and published in 1834 as the reform movement gathered pace, seems to oppose this view, however.

For the next 20 years the government and the whole medical profession were involved in abortive attempts at reform and the College was inevitably concerned about the direction this would take. But it had its own ideas about the internal changes that were needed and several drafts of a new charter were produced in this period. It was not until 1858 that a bill that was reasonably satisfactory to all parties managed to pass Parliament.

The Medical Act of 1858 overcame the problem of the numerous competing degree-granting and licensing bodies by setting up the semi-independent umbrella organisation with national responsibilities, the General Medical Council (GMC). Its purpose was to monitor the educational standards of all medical qualifications and to grant entry to its Medical Register to persons who had acquired one of the approved qualifications. This system remains in place today, although it, too, is undergoing major reform with more emphasis to be placed on standards of medical competence.

With the establishment of the GMC the College ceased to be a licensing body and its qualifications, like those of the universities, other royal colleges and the Society of Apothecaries, were subject to the approval of the new Council. The old Licentiates officially became Members (for some years many had frequently called themselves Members, especially on the title-pages of their publications and even the College was using the terms interchangeably in its *Annals* in the 1850s). The Extra-Licence was now redundant and holders of that diploma could also become Members on presenting satisfactory testimonials of character and paying the requisite fee.

One section of the Act proposed the granting of a new charter under which the name of the College could be changed to 'Royal College of Physicians of England'. It also suggested that any Licentiate or Member of Royal Colleges of Physicians of Edinburgh and Ireland practising in England should become a Member of the London College on payment of a fee. The London College objected that its Edinburgh counterpart had admitted some Licentiates without an examination, a provision intended only for 'good practitioners' of mature years but seen as a loophole through which inadequately trained men could get in. The three colleges conferred in 1860 but no reciprocal Membership transpired from their deliberations.

In 1860 the eight Elects, who up to that point had chosen the President *in camera* from among themselves, were abolished. From then, the President was to be chosen (annually as before) by all the Fellows present at the election on the day after Palm Sunday – the day is specified in the Medical Act, Royal Colleges of Physicians, 1860 – a practice that continues today. After all the discussions had taken place and constitutional changes made, the new *Bye-laws* were published in 1862, in English for the first time.

The College went on to establish its new undergraduate licence (LRCP Lond.) but not without some opposition from the Fellows. This licence was aimed at general practitioners, so it was necessary to allow those who obtained it to dispense medicines, previously strictly forbidden to everyone with College qualifications. After lengthy negotiations between the College and the Royal College of Surgeons of England, and objections by other bodies, this licence was joined in 1884 with the MRCS Eng. to create a joint qualification, both parts of which, like a university bachelor of medicine and surgery, had to be passed. The days when it was possible to obtain a qualification in one branch of medicine and practise in any other were coming to an end.

In 1883 the College was persuaded by the GMC, in spite of its reluctance to be involved in any kind of specialism, to offer a postgraduate Diploma in Public Health, so named when it was formalised in 1886 and transferred to the 'Conjoint Board' that ran the LRCP Lond./MRCS Eng. The Board introduced several other specialist diplomas in the late nineteenth and early twentieth centuries.

The Membership established itself as a necessary qualification for a career as a consultant and was at first the only route to the Fellowship. The bye-laws that permit the College to incorporate distinguished doctors from other disciplines into its ranks date from the twentieth century, and most from the period after World War II.

The 1858 Act removed another responsibility from the Royal Colleges, that of providing the nation's standard drug formularies [see pages 51–2]. The three separate pharmacopoeias – of London, Edinburgh and Dublin – were replaced by the *British pharmacopoeia*, compiled and published by the GMC. The first edition, published in 1864, was condemned as faulty by most and even 'dangerous' by the then President, Sir Thomas Watson, but the second edition of 1867 was generally accepted. That year, however, saw the publication of the *Nomenclature of diseases* [see page 52], so as the College relinquished the right to produce one set of standards, it undertook a different one.

The *Nomenclature* is part of the College's successful contribution to the field of public health and epidemiology. From the beginning, the College required the highest standards for individual patient care but its record on public health is less solid. In addition to its advice on the plague in the seventeenth century,

The title page of the Nomenclature of diseases, *published in 1869.*

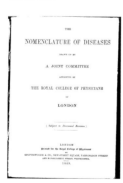

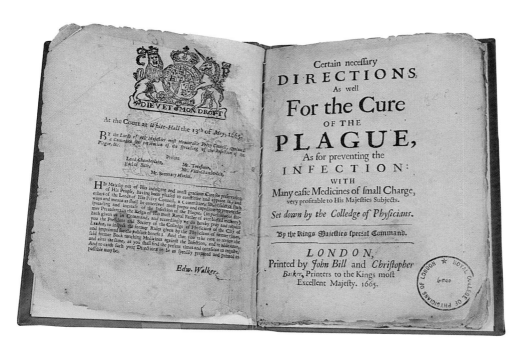

Certain necessary directions as well for the cure of the plague, as for preventing the infection, *1665. The remedies therein are described as 'very profitable to His Majesties Subjects'.*

in 1725 it petitioned Parliament on the evils of the excessive consumption of 'distilled spirituous liquors', mainly cheap gin. It tried to learn what it could about the severe influenza epidemic of the 1780s by inviting observations from medical men around the country. And it had quickly seen the value of vaccination in the early nineteenth century.

But when the attack began on the problems of sanitation aggravated by the uncontrolled growth of towns during the period of rapid industrialisation the College was not involved. Edwin Chadwick, the author of the *Report on the sanitary condition of the labouring population of Great Britain*, published in 1842, did not expect it to be. His solution lay in improving the infrastructure and he did not believe doctors had many useful ideas to contribute.

Gavin Milroy. Photograph by Moira and Haigh, 1864.

The College appointed a standing committee on sanitary questions in 1851, but apparently with minimal impact, but its cholera committee met regularly during the epidemic of the early 1850s – following an initiative of 30 years previously. In 1829, the College had attempted to survey the incidence of disease in various parts of the world in relation to climate, topography and physiology of the inhabitants. Later the Colonial Office sought its advice on diseases in Britain's overseas possessions, notably on leprosy in the West Indies, whereupon the College undertook to survey leprosy in all the colonies and dominions and published its report in 1867.

A leading figure in these activities was Gavin Milroy, who was among the Fellows of the College prominent in the Epidemiological Society, founded in 1850 and who endowed a College lecture on 'state medicine and public hygiene'. But these individual initiatives aside, real progress was not made until the College joined the Glasgow and Edinburgh Colleges to bring together the specialists in a Faculty of Public Health Medicine.

The Twentieth Century

Lord Dawson of Penn (1864–1945). Oils on canvas by Philip de Laszlo, 1937.

Examination and assessment, always one of the College's core activities, occupied even more of its attention from the late nineteenth century onwards than before. The number of candidates for the Membership increased and the diploma-granting activities of the 'Conjoint Board' (or the Examining Board in England to give it its official title) expanded – solid but uninspiring achievements.

There was a feeling in the late 1920s and early 1930s that the College was not a particularly dynamic organisation. Dr Charles Newman (MRCP 1928, FRCP 1932), a College enthusiast if ever there was one, used to describe the College when he first entered it as 'inert', although he witnessed huge changes up to the time when he relinquished the Harveian Librarianship in 1979.

Lord Dawson of Penn, President 1931–8, physician to four successive monarchs and the first medical consultant to be elevated to the peerage while still practising, attempted to increase the College's influence in the wider medical world and to give younger Fellows a greater voice in College affairs. A number of young men in their early to middle thirties, and the first women, were also elected to the Fellowship during his Presidency. Dawson's Cavendish lectures of 1918, expanded in the 1920 *Interim report on the future provision of medical and allied services* of the Ministry of Health's Consultative Council on Medical and Allied Services, which he chaired, was the first published plan for a comprehensive health service for Britain.

That aside, the lack of dynamism at the College was keenly felt at the outbreak of World War II. Dawson's successor, Sir Robert Hutchison, wanted to close the College down for the duration of hostilities, a move that provoked fury among the younger Fellows. They were dismayed that the College had minimal involvement in the arrangements for the emergency medical services. If the College remained aloof in a national crisis while the British Medical Association was actively involved in organising the emergency services, it would spell the end of any influence or reputation the College had with the government, the profession and the public.

The Younger Fellows' Club, with a maximum age 45, was formed to encourage the younger element to take an active part in College affairs and to work to augment the influence of the College. As a group it favoured the election of Sir Charles Wilson, later Lord Moran of Manton, as President in 1941. Moran had made it clear in 1938 that he thought that the College was not sufficiently concerned with important matters of medical policy when he addressed a 'Note on policy' to a group of Fellows. Among his complaints was the fact that the agendas of Comitia had never given the Fellows the opportunity to discuss wider issues, such as the introduction of clinical units into the London medical schools – something he had been involved with as Dean of St Mary's Hospital Medical School since 1920.

In Moran the Fellows elected a President who would work constructively with the government for the establishment of the National Health Service, in contrast to the hostile attitude adopted by many others in the medical profession [see pages 56–7].

With the gradual increase in the number of Fellows, through the first half of the century, the College's premises were feeling decidedly cramped and there was no room for expansion on the Trafalgar Square site. The Canadian High Commission, which had taken over from the Union Club, the southern half of the building designed in 1825 by Sir Robert Smirke, had suggested as early as 1923 that it would like to occupy the whole block if the College could find another home. A suitable alternative had not been found, however, when the 1939–45 War intervened.

Afterwards, a government committee led by Lord Gorell looked at the bomb damage in Regent's Park and concluded that as much as possible of the Nash terraces should be restored. However, it also conceded that the much altered small villa, Someries House, at the south-east corner and the French-style Cambridge Gate need not be retained: this would suit the College admirably. The Crown Estate Commissioners offered the Someries House site in 1958 and the College's Building Advisory Committee under the chairmanship of the President Robert Platt [see pages 68, 153] interviewed five architects. Denys Lasdun was appointed in September 1958. (Cambridge Gate is still there and was given a complete interior refurbishment in the 1990s.)

With a generous payment from the Canadians for the lease of the Trafalgar Square building, plus a donation of £450,000 from the Wolfson Foundation, and further donations from Fellows, the College was able to obtain the £750,000 to pay for its present building. It was opened in 1964 and listed Grade I in 1998 [see page 69]. It now had proper conference facilities and an adequate suite of offices, enabling it to escape from the situation where public rooms had also to serve for administrative purposes.

The move to a more open and modern building was symptomatic of a changing attitude in the College. Its reports on smoking, addressed to the public at large rather than the government or the medical profession alone, were ground-breaking in many respects. Visitors to the College today often have to make their way through ranks of smokers banished to the outside world, before they reach the main entrance and the clean air and lines of the interior. However unwholesome the sight, it is a striking and dynamic metaphor for the College's position on the issue that is repeated outside many buildings all over the country.

However, 20 years after arriving in Regent's Park, the College began to outgrow the facilities. Luckily, when 1–8 St Andrews Place became vacant the College was able to obtain the lease in the face of competition from other organisations, and 9–10 became available for overnight accommodation. The expansion involved hard work, especially on the part of the Treasurer, Dr Nigel Compston (1970–85), and the College Secretary, Michael Tibbs (1968–86). The terrace of houses dating from the 1820s, viewed across the garden, had been part of Lasdun's inspiration when he placed the large windows on the south side. The College now needed to raise over £4m to

Lord Platt of Grindleford (1900–78). Oils on canvas by Merlyn Evans, 1963.

21

The front of the College's St Andrews Place building, designed by Lasdun.

restore St Andrews Place to its original Nash vision and to cure the structural problems that had accumulated over the years.

The work was completed in 1985 and officially opened and designated as a Medical Precinct by HM The Queen in June 1986. Several parts were sublet to specialist medical societies, but as the years have passed the College has taken over their leases, as it has found the need for further office space. The College had hoped the British Paediatric Association, which was occupying most of No.5, would become a faculty under the joint aegis of the UK Royal Colleges of Physicians rather than a separate college. But when it became the Royal College of Paediatrics and Child Health in 1996 and decided it needed larger premises, the College was happy to absorb the vacated space.

Expanding educational needs have now led to the building of a new unit, the Jerwood Medical Education Centre, begun in the year 2000 in Peto Place, behind numbers 1–8 St Andrews Place. It will be a centre for distance learning and web-based education and training packages, as well as offering courses and workshops, and providing flexible teaching spaces and audio-visual back-up facilities.

The College also realised that it needed additional meeting spaces. The original 300-seat lecture theatre, named the Wolfson Theatre in 1996, proved too large for many purposes, both the College's own and those of the organisations hiring its facilities. An extension on the north side of the 1964 building was constructed in 1995–6 to Sir Denys Lasdun's design, which provided the 140-seat Seligman lecture theatre entered at the garden level, with a council chamber as its upper storey. The Wolfson Foundation was again prominent in the financing of this project along with the Welton Foundation, in memory of its trustee Geoffrey Seligman (1913–94), Hon.MRCP, a Friend of the College.

Hospital building programmes, the medical and scientific and technical discoveries of the twentieth century, and increasing specialisation have all added to the numbers of consultant doctors employed in the NHS. The numbers of Fellows and Members have continued to grow and the activities of the College to diversify, making ever increasing demands on office and meeting space.

Shortly after the move to St Andrews Place the College leaders concluded that the Fellowship was limited to too small a percentage of the country's consultant population. In the late 1960s under Max Rosenheim's presidency a recommendation was made that at least 200 should be elected annually. Since then numbers have increased to the point where there may be over 700 new Fellows in a year, reaching a total in the year 2000 of nearly 9,000 working all over the world.

The criteria for election to the Fellowship have been reconsidered a number of times. When calls have been made for Members to be given a greater say in the governance of the College, the response has been to widen the basis of the Fellowship. In 1946 a Standing Committee of Members was formed with the encouragement of Lord Moran and its members represented the younger element of the profession on Council, and on standing committees and working parties until the Committee was disbanded in 1999 following changes recommended by the James report [see page 25].

In the 1960s the Edinburgh, Glasgow and London colleges of physicians sensibly concluded that it was pointless to duplicate each others' efforts by offering rival Membership qualifications (100 years after preliminary moves were made along these lines). A common Membership examination (part 1 in 1968 and part 2 in 1972), supervised by a board of the three Colleges (with the Irish College involved in Part 1) was set up with the administration of the MRCP(UK) based in London.

The twentieth century, especially the latter half, saw a proliferation of medical colleges and specialist societies but also steadily increasing co-operation between them. The new colleges, unlike the already existing physicians' and surgeons' Colleges of England and Scotland, cover the whole of the United Kingdom. The first was the Royal College of Obstetricians and Gynaecologists, founded in 1929, and the latest, the Royal College of Paediatrics and Child Health, has been mentioned already.

Comitia 1968, *oils on canvas by Raymond Piper.*
The artist was present at three or four quarterly meetings of Comitia and Fellows were asked to sit in approximately the same place each time they attended if possible. The names of most of the Fellows in the painting are known, but a few of the smaller faces in the back rows have proved impossible to identify.

The co-operation between the physicians' Colleges of London, Edinburgh and Glasgow (as far as the latter is concerned with physicians) to examine and preside over postgraduate training has already been noted. The joint faculties of public health and pharmaceutical medicine also emerged from the combined actions of the three physicians' Colleges and together with the Royal College of Surgeons of England a Faculty of Accident and Emergency Medicine was also established.

Having confirmed their right to represent their specialties, these bodies co-operated increasingly on matters of mutual interest. In 1976 they launched the Conference (later renamed Academy) of Medical Royal Colleges and their Faculties, which early in its life produced an important report on brain death. Joint conferences and publications from joint working parties of both Colleges and specialist societies were a feature of the last decades of the twentieth century.

The College's own committees and working parties have also addressed questions on which alone it would not have been competent to pronounce, and have frequently included members of other organisations, a development that would have been unlikely before 1950. In the year 2000 it has even sought closer co-operation with the organisation that was once its deadly rival: the British Medical Association. Lord Moran would be astounded if he knew.

The growing numbers of Fellows and Members, the reorganisation of the NHS that successive governments have imposed, the increasing numbers of developments in medicine and the attendant problems of education and standardisation have led to the need for changes in the way the College is run. It was clear by the time of Dame Margaret Turner-Warwick's presidency that there was too much business for the quarterly Comitia of all the Fellows (conveniently) to manage. The geographical spread of the Fellowship together with their heavy NHS commitments meant that only a small minority of the Fellows were able to attend what had been for around 450 years the ruling committee of the College.

Much more responsibility was delegated to Council and four boards were created to consider various aspects of the College's regular business and report to Council: the Censors' Board (examinations, Membership), a Clinical Standards Advisory Board and a Paediatric Board (the latter disbanding after the paediatricians formed their own Royal College in 1996), and a Finance and General Purposes Board (including advisers from the financial world outside the College). Since 1999 there have been six boards, the Censors' Board now being renamed the Education Training and Examination Board [see Glossary]. In 1994 quarterly Comitia was abandoned and the final arbiter of policy is now the annual general meeting on 'College Day', coinciding with the election of the President and a symposium on a topic of primary interest to the Fellows.

The new boards were established along with a new management structure as a result of the recommendations of the 1998 report of the Working Party on Functions and Structures of the Royal College of Physicians under the chair-

Dame Margaret Turner-Warwick (PRCP 1989–92). Oils on canvas by David Poole, 1992.

manship of Professor Oliver James. The report acknowledged that the changes made in recent decades had achieved much in the way of increasing the College's activity and influence but that its purpose and core functions were not entirely clear, either to the profession or the public. Its relationships with other colleges and specialist societies, the committee thought, could be improved.

Trainees, its potential Members and Fellows of the future, and many consultants outside London still saw it as remote and inflexible despite its having developed a national network of College tutors and regional advisers. Acting on the report's recommendations the College, under the presidency of Sir George Alberti, has now established a network of regional offices through which it can provide permanent support for the educational and professional needs of trainee and practising consultant physicians. The new Jerwood education centre is intended to increase the College's ability to carry this work into effect. And the system of education, training and assessment that the College put into place in the early years of the twenty-first century should, for consultant physicians, meet the public's desire for the continuous assessment of the competence of doctors. There seem to be good prospects that the aims of the College, the government and the public might coincide as never before.

2

Themes in History

When Did the College Become Royal?

'When did the College become Royal?' is frequently asked by people who have noticed the absence of the word 'royal' from the College's name in old books and in its own official documents. They naturally assume that its addition must signify an official change of status at some point in the past. In fact, the College was established by a charter from Henry VIII so it was a royal foundation from the beginning, which is not really a satisfactory answer and rather confuses the issue.

The Charter of 1518 and the Act of Parliament of 1523 that confirmed its foundation referred to a faculty or commonalty or college of physicians in London – but with no place for 'royal'. The first suggestion that there should be something in the title of the College to denote the royal connection appeared over a century later, in the Charter granted by King Charles II in March 1663. This one referred to 'The President Fellows and Commonaltie of the King's College of Physitians in the Cittie of London'. Ironically, this charter was not ratified by Parliament and so never had the force of law, but the College seems to have taken the hint.

Daniel Whistler (1619–84). Oils on canvas, artist unknown, c.1660/70.

Both the College's chemist, William Johnson in 1665, and a Fellow, John Twysden in 1666, used the phrase 'King's College of Physicians' in their books defending the College against its critics. The Registrar's appeal for donations towards the new College building in Warwick Lane, transcribed into the *Annals* in September 1674, included the first documented use of 'royal'. He ended his letter to the Fellows with the words, 'Daniel Whistler, Registrar of the Royal College of Physicians of London' [see also page 144].

Then in February 1675 King Charles wrote to the President and Fellows twice using the phrase 'our Royal Colledge' and in 1677 the third revision of the College's pharmacopoeia appeared with the title, *Pharmacopoeia Collegii Regalis Londini* – the word '*regalis*' (royal) added for the first time. A few years later, in 1682, the College described itself in its *Annals* as 'Royal College of Physicians of London', when it decided that the names of its Fellows,

Licentiates, etc., should be printed immediately underneath. (Although the 1683 list uses the word 'King's', lists from 1688 on were printed under the heading 'Royal College of Physicians, London'.)

Dr Charles Goodall, having previously written *The College of Physicians vindicated*, published his extended apologia for the College's rights and privileges in 1684 under the title *The Royal College of Physicians founded and established by law*. Outside the College this trend had been observed elsewhere: lists of the current Fellows and Licentiates published without the College's authority between 1673 and 1681 referred to the 'King's College of Physicians in London'.

The College's 1663 Charter was issued eight months after the first charter of King Charles's new creation, the Royal Society, which had the 'royal' designation as an integral part of its name from the outset. Dr Whistler was made a Fellow of the Royal Society in that year. Meanwhile, the Royal College of Physicians of Edinburgh was established with that name by its 'Charter of Erection' of 1681 (Charles II) and confirmed by its 1685 'Charter of Ratification' from James II.

What seems clear is that the King in the post-Civil War interregnum wished to ensure that such organisations, founded by royal charter, remembered to whom they owed their allegiance. At the same time the London College no doubt hoped to erase if possible memories of its willing co-operation with the Parliamentary and Commonwealth authorities and to express its loyalty to the restored monarch [see pages 101–3].

But this is not the end of the story. Despite the increasing use of the 'royal' epithet during the eighteenth century by the College and others (the *Medical Register* of 1779, 1780 and 1783, for example, invariably described the College as 'royal') its appearance remained inconsistent right up to the mid-nineteenth century. The College's first journal was published in 1768 with the title *Medical Transactions published by the College of Physicians in London*. Two years before, when the College published the complete works of William Harvey in Latin, it had not thought it necessary to call itself royal on the title page. Nor did 'royal' (*regalis*) appear in the title of any of the printed or manuscript editions of the statutes (the predecessor of the *Bye-laws*) [see pages 103–5]. And it was still absent in 1834 when the then current version was printed in the Parliamentary Select Committee on Medical Education's report [see page 44].

By the time the Medical Act of 1858 and the Medical Act, Royal Colleges of Physicians 1860 were passed, however, 'Royal College of Physicians of London' had come to be accepted as the full title. Both Acts offered the option of changing it to 'Royal College of Physicians of England' by a new charter, but as that was never applied for and neither Act had stated categorically what the name was to be, the title had still not received statutory confirmation.

There was probably an element of competition between the Colleges over their royal connections. The Royal College of Surgeons of Edinburgh, for example, was so named by royal Charter of 1778, and the Royal College of Surgeons of England was named in its first royal Charter of 1800 'The Royal

The title page of the 1693 edition of the College statutes.

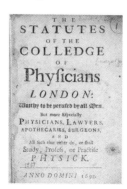

A section of the Charles II Charter, granted in March 1663.

College of Surgeons in London'. However, after the 1858 Act the Royal College of Physicians made a number of internal changes and then revised its bye-laws and published them in English for the first time, using the name by then generally agreed to be the correct one. This it has done consistently in all its official productions from that point on.

When the College acquired the Regent's Park site (in the London Borough of Camden) and realised that an Act of Parliament was needed to enable it to locate its headquarters outside the Cities of London and Westminster, it took the opportunity to get its name legally confirmed, by an appropriate clause in the Royal College of Physicians of London Act of 1960.

Fines and Fortunes:
Recognition and Regulation of Practitioners
for the First 200 Years

From its earliest days the College of Physicians had several purposes, but its most public one lay in its legal authority to determine which practitioners should be allowed to practise in the City of London and within seven miles of its walls. Its statutory powers gave it two means: the first required physicians to become a Fellow (or Candidate for the Fellowship); the second required those not able to become Fellows to obtain the College licence.

In fact, many ordinary practitioners who neither controverted the College nor angered their patients never came before the Censors' board for either kind of affiliation; but when the officers of the College wished, they could use their juridical authority to force compliance or to exact punishment.

Candidates for admission had to have obtained a medical doctorate and (following the Reformation) the degree had to be granted by or incorporated in one of the two English universities in order to ensure religious conformity. From the 1570s, votes on admission were taken at the quarterly meetings of the College after the Candidate had paid a visit to each of the Fellows and also after he had passed a formal three-part examination. And after James Stuart became king, so that his Scottish physicians could be admitted, Fellows had to be British subjects. To become a Fellow, therefore, one had to be of good character (British, nominally Anglican, and clubbable) and learned (both university educated and approved by the Censors).

Physicians were sometimes turned down for insufficient or incorrect learning. In 1555, President John Caius (of Cambridge) sent a letter to the Vice-Chancellor and Senate of Oxford complaining that they had granted an MB and an MD to two men found by the College's examination to be 'illiterate'. The return letter told the College that Oxford's judgement took precedence. But the Lord Chancellor, Cardinal Pole, sided with the College, and during a visit to Oxford established a more regular course of study for the MD.

A hint of the reasons for the controversy is revealed when John Geynes (DM Oxon 1535) sought admission in 1560, only to be subjected to a public three-day disputation, at the end of which he had to sign a document recanting his opinion that Galen had erred. Robert Fludd, a famous and powerful advocate of alchemical and Rosicrucian views and also a critic of Galenism, had a rather bumpy ride. At first he was rejected on examination before eventually being admitted a Candidate, only to be then expelled because of his frequent 'insolence'. He finally became a Fellow in 1609.

Some physicians tried to practise without the College's licence. Thomas Bonham (MD Cantab) for instance, was ordered to come to the College for examination, and was turned down. He earned first a heavy fine and then imprisonment for continuing to practise. After several years of legal wrangling, in February 1609 the College won its suit against Bonham in the Court of King's Bench. But Bonham in turn won his suit against the College in Common Pleas when Chief Justice Coke declared that the College had been unjust in proceeding against a university-educated physician. The King and courts later sided with King's Bench over Common Pleas: although occasionally physicians tried to argue that their university degree took precedence over the College's examination, the courts held for the College over the universities.

College Licentiates could also trouble the officers. They were non-voting Members of the College who could attend meetings, but because they were either foreigners, or had foreign degrees, or did not possess medical doctorates, they could not become Fellows. The Licentiates constituted a growing body of members – about 20 per cent of the College membership in 1650 and almost 50 per cent in 1695. They had less personal investment in the academic authority of physicians. Thus, when in the 1690s several Licentiates began to argue with the strict policies the officers were intent on establishing to control other medical practitioners, the disputes grew very hot (in a prelude to the revolt of the 1760s) with a few of the Fellows also siding with the Licentiates.

In one of the most controversial arguments that lasted for several years, the officers tried, fined, and finally imprisoned a Licentiate, Joannes Groenevelt, who dealt in a secret remedy for urinary problems. The upshot of the legal tangle was a draw: the College's proceedings against him found him not guilty while they were found not guilty in his suit against them. But by 1704 the attacks and counter-attacks brought both the College and Groenevelt into public disrepute.

The most controversial decisions about medical competence arose from struggles between the Censors and ordinary practitioners. The first record of fines for practice without the College's licence is in 1541, when the Court of Exchequer acted twice. By the 1570s, the President and Censors themselves heard cases against illicit practitioners and also against those who practised badly. It is worth observing that the rises and falls of College prosecutorial activity against the many unlicensed practitioners in London appears to be

29

better correlated with periods when the Crown supported the College as a policing institution than with shifting numbers of illicit practitioners themselves.

Many of the illicit practitioners were apothecaries and surgeons. The Barber-Surgeons Company and the Society of Apothecaries therefore used their influence at court, in Parliament, and in the City on behalf of their Members to try to limit the public authority of the College. At the end of the seventeenth century, the apothecaries obtained the right to be relieved of minor City obligations because they visited patients: this led to a counter-attack by the College via the Dispensary [see below].

It also led to the College's attempt to make an example of William Rose, apothecary, who had treated a butcher for syphilis. In early 1704, however, much to the surprise and dismay of the College, the Fellows lost the debate in the House of Lords, which allowed apothecaries to continue giving medical advice. Given the growth in power of popular opinion (which had been frequently opposed to the College's regulatory authority), within a few more years the College dropped its attempts to regulate outsiders.

Discord Over the Dispensary: Physicians and Apothecaries at War

When Dr Samuel Garth gave his Harveian Oration at the College in 1697, he concluded with a paragraph on a question that was causing considerable discord in the College. He stated that the profession's 'mutual love and affection' had been severely disrupted and he earnestly entreated Fellows to return to 'unitie and concord'.

He was referring to the controversy within the College about the repository, well furnished with drugs for the help of the poor, which the College had decided to establish in 1696, following the advice of its committee of medicines. The repository had not only caused friction among Fellows, but it also brought the College into direct conflict with the Society of Apothecaries, whose opposition, supported by some Fellows of the College, was vociferous and unyielding.

An uneasy relationship had existed between physician and apothecary throughout the seventeenth century and it had occasionally flared up into open hostility. The apothecaries had originally been part of the Grocers' Company but in 1617, under a royal charter granted by James I, they had established the Society of the Art and Mystery of Apothecaries of London. The apothecaries were to restrict their activities to the preparation and sale of drugs and yet be subservient to the physicians, who alone were allowed to treat patients. Moreover, the new Society had to consult with the College of Physicians before it adopted any new drug regulations or admitted new members.

There were, however, far too few physicians to deal with the increasing population of London and as the century went on, growing numbers of apothecaries began to prescribe medicines as well as preparing them – in response to public demand. Two other issues were influential in changing the role of the apothecary: politics and plague.

During the Civil War, many of the physicians, like William Harvey, were Royalists and during the Commonwealth the College of Physicians found it increasingly hard to regulate practitioners in the City. So, as the London apothecaries increasingly undertook treatment there was little that the College could do about what it described as 'the daring practices of the apothecaries'.

After the Restoration of Charles II in 1660, however, the College was able to assert its authority and in 1663 a new charter enhanced its powers of regulation over the apothecaries. Two years later, however, the city was struck by the Great Plague. The handful of physicians then living in the city, who claimed that they could treat the condition, were woefully ill-equipped both in numbers and knowledge to deal with a disaster which killed a third of the city's inhabitants. This led to a great increase in the number of apothecaries attempting to treat patients (although no better than the physicians) in addition to preparing drugs.

For years afterwards, the apothecaries were able with justification to attack the physicians for leaving the stricken capital since many of them fled, along with the court and their wealthy patients. The physicians countered by charging the apothecaries with enriching themselves during the plague at the expense of the sick and suffering.

The battle between physician and apothecary was conducted by tract and counter-tract for the remainder of the seventeenth century. During this time the physicians developed the idea, possibly induced in part by a sense of guilt at their behaviour during the plague, that there should be a public clinic supported by the College. This was first suggested in 1670, but it was not until 1687 that the College formally announced that its members would give free treatment to any certified pauper. It was followed by the proposal that there should be a public dispensary at the College, where medicines would be provided free for the sick poor.

This was construed by the apothecaries to be a direct threat to their livelihood as well as an intrusion into their work as established by their charter. Some physicians sympathised with the apothecaries and a group of physicians emerged which opposed the College plans.

By 1696, however, the College committee on medicines proposed that the dispensary should go ahead with free medicines for the poor. By the end of the year, 52 members, including Hans Sloane, Samuel Garth and the President of the College, Sir Thomas Millington, had subscribed £10 each towards the venture. It was the discord in the College between those who supported or opposed the dispensary that had prompted Garth's exhortation in his Oration.

In the spring of 1698 the dispensary was opened at the College in Warwick Lane and it was so successful that two more dispensaries were opened, one

Sir Samuel Garth (1661–1719). Oils on canvas from the studio of Sir Godfrey Kneller. (Copy of Kneller's portrait c.1710 for the Kit-cat club.)

A document printed in 1697 to explain the College's reasons for establishing its dispensaries.

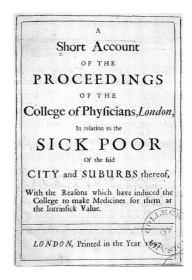

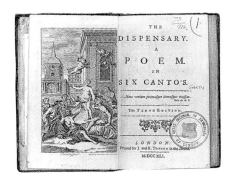

The title spread of the tenth edition of Garth's poem The Dispensary, *1741.*

in St Martin's Lane, the other in Gracechurch Street – the first public dispensaries for the poor to be established in this country.

Opposition by the antidispensarians, however, continued unabated and it was not until a year later that Garth, with the publication of his famous poem *The Dispensary* in 1699, all but ended the dispute. Written in mock-heroic style, later to be refined by Alexander Pope, the poem describes a comic and trivial event in a lofty and classical poetic style. The trivial event was the battle between the College and the apothecaries. Garth made his poem particularly comic in modelling his characters on known individuals, easily recognised by the physicians and apothecaries of the day.

Colon was an apothecary called Lee, Horoscope was Dr Bernard, Mirmillo the antidispensarian physician Dr William Gibbons and there are others such as Querpo who was a Dr How. The main feature of the poem is a disreputable battle between physicians and apothecaries during which a whole range of medical paraphernalia is used. 'Pestles', wrote Garth, 'peel a martial symphony.' The apothecaries begin to gain the day and Querpo is on the point of slaying Stentor – thought to be Dr Charles Goodall, leader of the physicians – when Apollo assumes the form of Fee, at which Querpo instinctively snatches instead of striking the fatal blow. In the final stanzas, the fighting ceases when Hygeia, the goddess of health appears and bids Machaon (Sir Thomas Millington, President of the College) to send Carus (who is Dr Tyson) to accompany her to the Elysian Fields to consult William Harvey. They meet with the horrifying inhabitants of the underworld: Old Chaos, an awkward Lump of shapeless Anarchy, with dull Night, his melancholy consort; pale Fear and dark Distress, parched Ey'd Febris,

> Then Hydrops next appears amongst the Throng,
> Bloated and big, she slowly sails along,
> But like a Miser in Excess she's poor
> And pines for Thirst amidst her watery Store.

They meet meagre Phthisis, Lepra the loathsome, as well as other sights that go to make up the frightful horror of the place, but at last they are ferried across the Styx and find the shade of William Harvey. He addresses Hygeia, referring to the dissent within the faculty:

> Where Sickening art now hangs her Head
> And once a Science is become a Trade;

then to Carus to whom he turns with the admonition that by attending to science more and to lucre less and by letting Nassau's – that is King William's or England's – health be its chief aim, the College could once again become restored to the position it held under Willis and Wharton, Ent and Glisson. The poem ends with Carus and Hygeia returning to the College with this message.

The Dispensary had an importance which went far beyond its virtue as a work of art. It was an immediate and resounding success. Three editions were called for in the first year of its appearance; eight editions were published during Garth's lifetime (he died in 1718), and it was reprinted throughout the eighteenth century. Although two historians of the Society of Apothecaries give Garth the credit for having 'chased the opposition from the field', disputes between the physicians and apothecaries grumbled on until the famous case of William Rose as described in the previous chapter [see page 30].

Garth's poem not only had an important effect on a prolonged and undignified professional quarrel. It was also a unique contribution to English literature. It formed an indispensable link between the poetry of Dryden, who was much admired by Garth, and the grandeur of the Augustan age, represented in later years by Alexander Pope. Dryden himself read *The Dispensary* and referred to Garth as 'generous as his muse'.

When Dryden died in 1700, Garth was widely considered to be his poetic heir although in the ensuing years his poetic reputation fell dramatically. This was not only due to the emergence of Pope as the master of wit and epigram, but also because of the fickleness of poetic taste, the acclamation of one generation being quite likely, in Edmund Gosse's words, 'to be hooted out of Court by the next'. Garth's poetic output remained relatively modest, probably owing to his increasing professional commitments after the year 1700 and his developing popularity among the great and good of the day, including the Duke and Duchess of Marlborough.

Nonconformists and Other Outsiders

During the seventeenth century, stimulated by the Protestant ideals of the Reformation and the Puritan revolution, a number of Nonconformist sects emerged in England. Initially suffering severe persecution, including imprisonment, it was not until the next century that such sects began to be tolerated in English society.

The Baptists had appeared before the Civil War. Their preachers were to win many adherents around the campfires of Cromwell's army. Unitarianism, which adopted a doctrine of scriptural rationalism and rejected the concept of the Trinity, became established during the eighteenth century as did Methodism, which emerged from the Anglican Church and was led by John Wesley. The Quakers, or Society of Friends, had an older origin. It was derived from groups of Seekers who during the Puritan revolution determined to wait upon the Lord because they despaired of the spiritual help offered by either the Anglican Church or by other Puritan bodies such as the Baptists, Presbyterians and Congregationalists.

Nonconformist groups throughout the seventeenth and eighteenth centuries were bound by the Clarendon Code, which had been imposed during the early years after the restoration of Charles II. The Corporation Act forbade municipal office to those not taking the sacrament at a parish church and the Test Act barred all but Anglicans from any form of public office. Although the Toleration Acts of 1689 eased some of the constraints placed upon Nonconformists, many of the Acts of the Clarendon Code were not repealed until the nineteenth century.

A further limitation placed upon Nonconformists was that they were debarred from the English universities – Oxford and Cambridge – since they could not subscribe to the 39 articles of the Anglican Church. And it was this ruling that brought Nonconformist physicians into conflict with the College of Physicians because the College insisted on electing to its Fellowship only those who had an Oxford or Cambridge degree.

This proved something of an advantage to many Nonconformists who went instead to Continental universities such as Leyden, the foremost school of medicine in Europe until the death of Herman Boerhaave in 1738. The Leyden MD was highly regarded, and many of the physicians who staffed the newly founded voluntary hospitals in London during the first half of the eighteenth century were Leyden men. Later it was to be the Edinburgh medical school, founded in 1726 by four professors who were all pupils of Boerhaave, that inherited Leyden's position and which became an educational haven for the Nonconformist.

The first of the new Edinburgh medical graduates to obtain the Licentiateship of the College of Physicians, in 1744, was Dr John Fothergill, a Quaker who throughout his life was a supporter of radical causes. He was to be an influential figure among the Licentiates of the College who sought to establish their right to be elected to the Fellowship. In 1746, two years after Fothergill had become a Licentiate, there were 56 Fellows of the College and 24 Licentiates.

The numbers of the Licentiates, many of them Nonconformists, were gradually swollen by graduates of Edinburgh and of European universities such as Leyden, so that 40 years later the Licentiates had a majority over the Fellows of 73 to 40. There were repeated attempts by the Licentiates to establish their right to the Fellowship during those years. An attempt to overthrow the hegemony of the Fellows failed in 1750, their monopoly within the College being said by their critics to be maintained 'By a sham, grave sons of Isis and grave sons of Cam'.

In 1752 the Licentiates complained about their exclusion from all offices within the College, only to receive a blunt response that the College was within its rights. In 1765, the Licentiates brought a further lawsuit against the College that was heard by Lord Justice Mansfield. It too failed, but the Lord Justice warned the College that they were pursuing a narrow policy that would in its time have excluded the great Herman Boerhaave.

Matters became more serious in 1767 when the Licentiates formed themselves into a Society of Collegiate Physicians to pursue their grievances. They were a highly distinguished group of physicians. They included Dr John Fothergill, who by now had one of the most successful practices in London,

William Murray, 1st Earl of Mansfield, the Lord Chief Justice who in 1765 warned the College against its policy of excluding Licentiates from its offices.

Top: *'The March of the Medical Militants to the Siege of Warwick Lane Castle in the Year 1767'. Engraved by J. June, 1768.*

Above: *'The Siege of Warwick Castle; or The Battle between the Fellows and Licentiates'. Artist unknown.*

John Fothergill (1712–80). Etching, artist and date unknown.

Browne's jibe, in verse, at Scottish medical graduates, taken from his commonplace book, RCP MS 175.

William Hunter, physician brother of John, Sir William Watson, Huck Saunders, George Fordyce and John Elliot, afterwards a baronet and physician to the Prince of Wales. One half of the members were, or subsequently became, Fellows of the Royal Society.

The College, however, was adamant in maintaining the rules on the Fellowship and continued to exclude non-Oxbridge graduates from the affairs of the College. This provoked an attempt by the more violent of the Licentiates to break into a meeting of the Comitia of the College, its ruling body, employing a blacksmith to break open the doors which were barred against them. This too was unsuccessful and the President, Sir William Browne, remarked that: 'With inhuman violence they broke into this very senate, like swimming sea monsters in our medical ocean.'

The whole affair was brilliantly satirised by Samuel Foote in his play *The Devil upon two sticks*. In it the Quaker Fothergill was portrayed, much to his displeasure, as 'Dr Melchisedech Broadbrim', a reference to the size of the hat which, following Quaker custom, he did not remove even in the presence of his patients. Fothergill, true to the pacifism of his sect, took no part in the violence but contributed the sum of £500 to the costs involved. The Society of Collegiate Physicians continued to meet and Fothergill became President in 1772, serving until his death in 1780.

The College, however, steadfastly refused to relax its rules. There were occasional exceptions. Sir John Pringle, Edinburgh graduate and Unitarian, was elected to the Fellowship; but he had royal connections, having been with Cumberland at Culloden, and also President of the Royal Society. In 1771, however, Sir William Browne surprised the College Fellowship by proposing Fothergill. The proposal was defeated by 13 votes to 9.

In 1784, the President of the College was given permission to propose two Licentiates of ten years' standing for election as Fellows and in that same year Sir William Watson and Huck Saunders were elected. Thereafter, there were occasional elections of non-Oxbridge men to the Fellowship.

At the same time, the Society of Collegiate Physicians forgot its animosity towards the College, altering its rules to allow Fellows to be members of the Society and removing their boycott of the *Medical Transactions*, which they had upheld since 1767. The rules on admitting non-Oxbridge men to the Fellowship, however, were not formally changed until 1835, three years after the passage through Parliament of the Reform Bill.

Women's Place in the College

The history of women doctors and the Royal College of Physicians is closely linked to that of women in medicine more generally.

Over the past 5,000 years of medical history and before significant regulation of the profession, there is good documentation that women practised medicine. Women physicians are recorded on Egyptian inscriptions around 3000 BC and, more recently, women were accepted into some of the earliest European medical schools. They both studied and taught at Salerno in the ninth century and at Montpellier in the eleventh century and many aristocratic women are recorded as practising medicine in medieval Britain.

In later centuries there is contradictory evidence concerning women practising medicine. Women were often forbidden from training or practising on the basis of social and religious constraints, and yet there is ample documentation that they continued to do so – licensed and unlicensed – because of the practical need.

More recently, over the past 150 years, there have been well-intentioned attempts to regulate medical practice much more rigorously, mainly to improve standards of practice and very recently (over the past 20 years or so) in attempts to save costs of medical care in both the public and the private sector. The Medical Act of 1858 set up the General Medical Council as a self-regulatory body to implement and monitor standards of training. There were no restrictions in this Act on allowing women to present themselves for assessment and registration. It was largely the individual universities and medical schools in the UK who barred women from entry and training and thus *de facto* women were excluded from presenting themselves to the licensing bodies including the Royal College of Physicians.

The stimulus for change came from individual pioneering women. Unable to study medicine in England, Elizabeth Blackwell sought training in New York State and returned to England, challenged the authorities and became registered in 1859. Likewise Elizabeth Garrett (later Garrett Anderson 1836–1917) challenged the College in 1864 to be allowed to sit their licensing examination on the grounds that she wished to be examined on equal terms to men rather than through the easier route of the Society of Apothecaries. The College sought legal advice and refused on the alleged grounds that its bye-laws precluded the College from granting licences to practise to females and from admitting them to examination for a licence. She therefore resorted to the Society of Apothecaries, obtained a Licentiate (LSA) and in 1865 became the first woman to qualify in medicine in the UK.

Pressure for equal opportunities for women led to the Gurney Act of 1876 that removed the restrictions on qualifying for registration on grounds of sex. In line with this law, the General Medical Council even suggested that if licensing bodies would not lift their restrictions, then the Council itself would consider setting up a special qualifying examination for women. At this time just seven women were on the Register.

The College discussed the matter in 1878 and still refused to change its views – one individual suggesting 'that if girls were encouraged to use their brains the excitement caused thereby would produce insanity.' However, nearly 20 years later, following a petition from the London School of Medicine for Women (LSMW) and backed by women from the staff of the associated Royal Free Hospital, the College was again asked to reconsider the matter. By

Dr Helen Mackay, the College's first woman Fellow, admitted in 1934.

Dr Janet Vaughan, the first woman to be admitted to the Council, in 1943.

Dame Albertine Winner, appointed the Linacre Fellow of the College and the first woman College officer, in 1967.

Dame Sheila Sherlock, the first woman Censor, appointed in 1970. She went on to become the first woman Senior Censor and Vice-President in 1971.

this time there were about 200 women on the Register, 150 of them from the LSMW. But the College again refused.

After a further eight years the bye-laws were changed in 1909 to allow women to sit the LRCP and MRCP examinations and become Licentiates and Members of the College. However they were neither eligible for the Fellowship nor allowed to participate in the governance or management of the College.

The first woman to obtain the MRCP (introduced for men by the College in 1859) was Ivy Woodward (Mrs Haslam) in 1909. She was evidently an outstanding student and obtained the London University MD gold medal, a postgraduate degree taken by examination at that time. The first woman to obtain the LRCP (a qualifying examination for men since 1859 [see page 18]) was Miss Dossibhai Patell in 1910. Gradually other medical schools accepted women as medical students but it took another 50 years and the establishment of the National Health Service (1948) for all medical schools in the UK to do so.

Following national pressures for equal opportunities in education and suffrage augmented by the changing roles of women during and after World War I, the College eventually changed its bye-laws in 1925 to allow women to become Fellows and thereby participate in its governance and management. The existing Fellowship still managed to delay implementation of this for another nine years.

Eventually, in 1934 the first woman became a Fellow. In the light of later events it is noteworthy that the College elected an eminent paediatrician, Dr Helen Mackay, as its first woman Fellow. The first general physician was Dr Dorothy Christian Hare, elected Fellow in 1936. She was a general physician with interests in colitis, arthritis, diabetes and helped girls with venereal disease.

Progress remained slow and participation in the governance and management of the College was limited. It took another nine years for the first woman, Dr Janet Vaughan to be appointed to Council in 1943. She was also the first to give a College lecture – the Bradshaw Lecture in 1947.

World War II gave further impetus to the recognition of professional sex equality. Over the next 50 years the number of women entering medicine steadily increased. At the same time the College developed its role in many ways including supervision and coordination of postgraduate training programmes. Along with the Royal College of Physicians of Edinburgh and the Royal College of Physicians and Surgeons of Glasgow they established the Joint Committee for Higher Medical Training (JCHMT). Dame Albertine Winner played a central role in this for 11 years; she was appointed the Linacre Fellow of the College and the first woman College officer in 450 years – only 33 years ago.

The Senior Censor of the College leads a small group of Censors who are responsible for the MRCP examination and also serves as its Vice-President. Dame Sheila Sherlock was the first woman Censor appointed in 1970 and she went on to become the first woman Senior Censor and Vice-President in 1971. She was also the first woman to deliver the College's premier lecture – the Harveian Oration – in 1985, an annual event that had been established in 1656 but it had taken 329 years before it was delivered by a woman.

In 1989, 471 years after its foundation, the Fellows of the College elected their first woman President – Dame Margaret Turner-Warwick (DBE in 1991). She was also the second woman to deliver the Harveian Oration, in 1994. These 'firsts' give some insight into the background of acceptance of women by the College.

Of much greater importance is the fact that once women had been offered and accepted these senior posts, the College has a fine record of giving them a generous welcome in a spirit of equal partnership on important medical business, which has nothing to do with gender.

Over the last decade progress towards professional equality has increased in several ways. The number of women Fellows has steadily increased. In 1980 just 19 women were elected compared to 220 men (8 per cent); in 1999 they represented 23 per cent of UK Fellows. Since Fellows are of course elected almost exclusively from consultant physicians and about 17 per cent of women are currently represented nationally in this category, it is evident that women Fellows are now well supported by the College. And since the numbers of women consultants are rising dramatically in most medical specialties, we can expect a corresponding increase in women Fellows over the next few years.

At first sight it may seem disappointing that more women are not selected to give College lectures, but this in part may be due to the relative paucity of women in senior academic posts – which is also in part their choice – rather than to any College prejudice. Evidence of this is supported by the fact that in the newly founded Academy of Medical Sciences there are, in the year 2000, only about 25 women (8 per cent) out of around 330 holding a medical qualification.

Although the conservative attitude to women taken by the College in the nineteenth century is historically understandable it certainly could have taken a much more enlightened view when other bodies were prepared for and promoting change. However, progress over the last 50 years has been quite different and the record shows that by wisely ignoring gender in medical matters, equality of opportunity has been established between the sexes at all levels – for those taking the College examination and those appointed or elected to serve the College in many ways: in the year 2000 these included four Officers of the College as well as a number of women in senior management posts. The fact that it has done this without pandering to 'politically correct' pressures for women to receive special consideration, is all to its credit. It will be interesting to see what will happen if, as trends suggest, women become numerically the greater partner in medicine of the future.

Dame Margaret Turner-Warwick, the College's first woman President, elected in 1989.

Endowments and Education:
Development of Postgraduate Education

Thomas Linacre, College founder and first President.

In the early years, the founding Fellows were slow to appreciate the potential educational role for the College. Physicians gave little thought to any form of education outside the normal academic studies pursued earlier at university. The Royal College of Physicians of London expected physicians to have graduated at Oxford or Cambridge before presenting themselves for admittance, and at these universities the education of physicians was primarily literary rather than medical. Thus when Thomas Linacre, College founder and its first President, sought to improve medical education by leaving endowments he did so to Oxford and Cambridge rather than to the College in London.

The Charter for Anatomies

Nevertheless it is not entirely fair to say that the College was merely an examining and disciplinary body with absolutely no interest in education. Motivation for a limited degree of medical education came in 1565, when, under letters patent under the Great Seal, the College obtained the right each year to claim four bodies of hanged criminals for dissection. This became known as the Charter for Anatomies and the Fellows undertook to perform the dissections publicly in rotating order of seniority.

The Endowed Lectures

The founding of the Lumleian Trust in 1582 by Dr Richard Caldwell in association with John, Lord Lumley, started the long and distinguished tradition of endowed lectures in the College. Other early lecture series included the Goulstonian founded in 1635 from a bequest from Dr Theodore Goulston, and the Croonian established in 1701 by the widow of Dr William Croone. Initially they were not popular because busy professional men felt little need for further education. And this general view may explain why Harvey's revelation, that blood circulated rather than ebbed and flowed, provoked so little interest at the time. Nevertheless these endowed lectures were to form a major part of the College's educational programme for the next four centuries.

A section of the Charter for Anatomies, 1565.

Medicine – a Lifelong Study

Although the College was insistent on holding on to its examining privileges it showed little interest in the teaching of clinical medicine to doctors in career grades until the inception of the National Health Service.

This brought a new urgency to the problems of both undergraduate and postgraduate education. Under the Chairmanship of the President, Dr W. Russell Brain (later Lord Brain), a College Committee on Medical Teaching was set up in 1950. Although initially meetings were almost wholly concerned with undergraduate education, the committee soon turned its attention to the problems of postgraduate education.

Left: *the Lumleian Lectures deed, and,* above, *the inscription written on the back.*

It was acknowledged that it was no longer possible for anyone to obtain a comprehensive medical training during the years at medical school, a theme that was developed in the second conference on World Education in 1959 entitled 'Medicine – a lifelong study'.

Progress was slow and in a memorandum to the committee in 1965 Sir George Pickering was forced to point out that 'comparatively little has been done to think out, organise and develop postgraduate education.' He went on to add, 'proper organisation of graduate education would not be very expensive to the nation.' It was an optimistic but, for Sir George, not a particularly accurate forecast.

The burgeoning of non-collegiate postgraduate organisations throughout the 1950s and early 1960s led the College to refine its own role. At this time responsibility for postgraduate training was shared between universities, the Ministry of Health and all the royal colleges. Their coordination left much to be desired. The contemporary correspondence, often a little tetchy, betrayed the College's lingering suspicions about the ability of the newer organisations to provide medical education of the highest quality. The College was still determined to occupy centre stage.

The move to the new site in Regent's Park enabled it to do this. It began to sponsor many more conferences and scientific meetings to bring new advances to the notice of its Fellows and Members. The prestigious annual Consultant Conferences, started in 1964, proved extremely popular and still continue to attract large audiences.

But it was clear that if the College wanted to remain centre stage it had to extend its influence outside London by encouraging the growth of a network of postgraduate and continuing education facilities. The President, Professor Max Rosenheim (later Lord Rosenheim), took up this challenge and worked

Max Leonard Rosenheim, Baron Rosenheim of Camden (1908–72), PRCP 1966–72. Photograph taken at a press conference for the publication of Smoking and health now, *1971.*

41

'The Reward of Cruelty' by Hogarth, 1751. A view of a dissecting room derived partly from the Cutlerian Theatre, and partly from the Barber-Surgeons' anatomy theatre, showing the dissection of a hanged criminal. At the foot of the cartoon is a cautionary verse addressed to the criminal.

tirelessly, travelling extensively, opening and visiting new centres. The College's regional organisation was further strengthened in 1969 by the appointment of regional advisers and later by College tutors.

The education and training of doctors in the NHS demanded close liaison with other medical colleges and organisations within the UK and, following recommendations of the Royal Commission on Medical Education in 1968, the Joint Committee on Higher Medical Training (JCHMT) was set up. This committee took on board the mammoth task of approving training programmes and of monitoring the progress of trainees.

Continuing Medical Education

Pressures to introduce formal systems of continuing medical education built up in the late 1980s when doctors began to face criticism of their traditional methods of maintaining professional competence. As Chairman of the Education Committee, Professor Leslie Turnberg, later Lord Turnberg, set out the London College's views which later were incorporated in general principles agreed by the Conference of Medical Royal Colleges during the summer of 1993.

Dr Peter Toghill was appointed as Director of Continuing Medical Education in 1993 to oversee its development within the London College. With the corresponding directors in the sister colleges of Edinburgh and Glasgow a formal credit-based system was established and physicians were encouraged to participate in approved educational activities as a professional obligation, and to record these activities in personal diaries. In addition to their specialist knowledge it was recognised that doctors required an understanding of wider topics such as ethics, management, appraisal, peer review and communication skills (Continuing Professional Development).

Education Department

An awareness of the importance of the role of the College in the training of physicians in all grades led to the development of the education department under the directorship of Professor Lesley Rees in 1998 with Winnie Wade as Head of Education. Its purpose was to develop educational policy and initiatives. In 1999 it assumed the responsibility for administering the Education, Training and Examinations Board and the Examinations Committee.

As the College enters the new Millennium it aims to offer a comprehensive educational programme to prepare young doctors for their MRCP examinations, to coordinate their training, to advise and monitor Continuing Professional Development for those in the career grades and to bring the latest developments to the attention of all.

Lectures and Learning

Until the twentieth century the endowed lectures were the sum total of the College's involvement in postgraduate education [see page 40]. They, and the publications derived from them, provide an idiosyncratic glimpse of the development of medical research and scientific discoveries over three centuries. Early examples are Francis Glisson on the liver, *Anatomia hepatis* (1654), and Thomas Wharton's *Adenographia* (1656) on the glands from their Goulstonian lectures. In the nineteenth century Marshall Hall's expanded versions of his Croonian lecture of 1850 can be seen as a report on the latest thinking on reflex action.

William Croone (1633–84). Oils on canvas by Mary Beale, c.1680.

A map of Burmarsh, the estate given to the College by William Harvey to endow an annual feast and oration to promote good fellowship.

The anatomy lectures which were instituted by the 1565 Charter probably ceased as a discrete series in the late seventeenth century, by which time the Lumleian Lectures with their individual endowment were recognised as the principal anatomical and surgical lectures. Then Goulstonian Lectures were read on anatomy in relation to disease and the series was the College's first to focus on pathology.

In 1656 William Harvey [see also pages 70–1, 141–3] gave the estate of Burmarsh in Kent to the College to endow an annual feast and oration to promote fraternity amongst the Fellows. In the language of the day the event was intended to increase mutual affection among the Fellows for the better maintenance of the dignity of the profession. The orator was to commemorate the benefactors of the College and to encourage others to imitate their example. This style has continued to the present: in the twentieth century orators reviewed recent progress in some aspect of medicine and related this activity to Harvey's exhortation to 'search and study out the secrets of nature by way of experiment'.

A materia medica lecture briefly existed in the early nineteenth century, but it was in the late nineteenth and early twentieth centuries that many more lectureships were launched. Tuberculosis, the well-known scourge of the time, was a popular subject; originally the lecturer's remit was quite specific but it has now been broadened to cover chest diseases generally. Most lecturers are chosen by designated College officers although the lectureship founded by Gavin Milroy FRCP (1805–86) on 'State medicine and public hygiene' was, until the foundation of the Linacre lecture in 1990, for Fellows and Members under the age of 40, the only one for which applications were submitted.

In 1901 Dr (later Sir) Norman Moore persuaded the widow of Thomas FitzPatrick MRCP (1832–1900) to endow an annual lecture on medical history in memory of her husband. The bequest from David Lloyd Roberts FRCP (1835–1920) founded a lecture on a topic of general medical or scientific interest usually read by a lecturer who is not medically qualified. College lectures on similar lines have been a regular feature of new Members' evenings since 1995.

Evolution of the Examination: Membership by Examination from the Licence in 1836

During 1833–4, the stage was set for changes in the College's hierarchical structure by the deliberations of Henry Warburton's parliamentary committee on medical education. The committee had gathered a mass of evidence about the state of the College, including the anomalies and injustices that had been meted out to certain individuals. But, even before the committee reported, the

College had made a start in remedying the invidious position of the Licentiates of the College in comparison to that of the Fellows [see page 33–6].

By 1836 a thorough revision of the statutes had led to the introduction of more stringent conditions concerning age and length and quality of experience for candidates for the licensing examination. Furthermore, all successful candidates, regardless of whether they were Oxford or Cambridge graduates or not, became eligible to be proposed as Fellows after four years. For the next 20 years, therefore, the Licentiate was unequivocally a postgraduate qualification.

These two decades were full of abortive attempts in Parliament to produce acceptable legislation to regulate and organise the medical profession. The College, too, was alive to the idea of reform and, in 1852, a draft charter contained the first reference to Membership by examination. Following the enactment of the Medical Act of 1858, the College bye-laws were changed to create the tripartite system of Licentiates (equivalent to holders of a university MB), Members and Fellows. Existing Licentiates could become Members on application and all university graduates in medicine became eligible to enter for the new Membership examination; the first of these was held in April 1859.

The examination consisted of three written papers (reduced to two in 1867), a clinical and two orals. Passages for translation from Latin, Greek, French and German were also included. This opportunity to demonstrate the breadth of their expertise was taken by fewer and fewer candidates as the years went by and the classical languages eventually disappeared in 1936, although the French and German dimension existed until 1963.

For the first 100 years of the examination, no fundamental changes were made in the basic shape of the Membership, although from time to time committees were set up to consider various problems that had arisen. For example, from the later years of the nineteenth century, there were increasing numbers of distinguished physicians who, for one reason or another, had not obtained the Membership in their youth. Even the most eminent were required to take an examination although it might be restricted to a single oral only. However, a direct route to the Fellowship for such men was opened by the enactment of bye-law 39b. For those slightly less distinguished, direct election to the Membership on the recommendation of the Censors became possible in 1938.

During World War I, there had been a marked fall in the numbers of candidates but this was reversed during World War II. To meet the demand of medical officers in the forces the examination was held in Cairo and Poona in 1944.

The situation began to change even more in the 1950s. This was partly triggered by the dramatic increase in the number of candidates after the War and the heavy burden this imposed on examiners and other staff. Another was the increasing doubt about the reliability of the existing pattern of examinations in medicine as a means of testing knowledge particularly

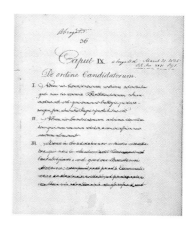

The page of the 1811 statutes (MS 2012/90) stipulating the requirement that all Fellows be Oxbridge-educated. The text was crossed out in 1835 when this proviso was dropped in favour of more stringent conditions based on the professional and academic merit of the applicant.

following an influential paper by Graham Bull in 1956. Accordingly, after a flurry of committee reports in the early 1960s, it was decided to institute a new Part 1 consisting of multiple-choice questions to eliminate candidates who were clearly not of the required standard.

In 1966, a study group took over from the Censors the setting and administration of this new examination. As a preliminary move towards the new diploma of MRCP (UK), which came into being in 1969, the London study group was replaced by the Joint Examining Board of the three UK colleges of physicians in 1968. Another change in London in the early 1960s was the institution of a Part 3 for paediatricians and psychiatrists. This was abolished in 1970 following the special arrangements for paediatricians in the new Part 2, and the foundation in 1971 of the Royal College of Psychiatrists.

From August 1969 all candidates who passed the Membership examination of any of the three Colleges, all of which included the common Part 1, were eligible for election as MRCP (UK). The total merger of the three examinations did not take place until after much discussion on the pattern of the Part 2. These began in the London College where a review committee put forward radical proposals in 1970 that were designed to increase the objectivity and, therefore, the reliability of the examination. Thus, the essay papers, having been largely replaced by Part 1 and known to be unreliable, were abandoned completely. A new written section was seen mainly as a replacement for the oral; problem-solving, interpretation of data and visual recognition were to be tested separately, the last by a series of slides shown to groups of candidates in turn (these were later replaced by photographs).

This raised the possibility of the abolition of the oral but a personal interview was thought by many to be valuable and the oral survived, but with strict constraints on the type of questions to be asked. Similar constraints were to apply to the clinical questions.

These proposals were accepted by a planning committee of the three Colleges, a committee that later became the Common Examining Board. Trials of the new written section with a group of Registrars who had already passed the examination and, later, a larger group of examiners as 'candidates' were successful and the whole new examination for the MRCP (UK) was in being by 1972. It served well for a generation. Following a recent comprehensive review Part 2 will be replaced in 2001 by a Practical Assessment of Clinical Examination Skills (PACES).

The first three Membership examination papers, April 1859. Top to bottom: *first paper* ('in parte physiologica'); *second paper* ('in parte pathologica'); *third paper* ('in parte therapeutica').

Research and Evaluation

The earliest and still the most notable piece of research carried out by a Fellow was William Harvey's on the circulation of the blood [see pages 141–3]. When he published his work in 1628, he stated in the 'Epistle dedicatory' that he had been demonstrating his experiments to a number of the

Fellows 'for nine years and more'. But the programme of research was Harvey's own and was conducted privately.

The Lumleian Lectures [see pages 40–1] that Harvey delivered for 40 years had been established for basic surgical teaching and involved cadavers, whereas Harvey needed living animals to test his hypotheses. Several of Harvey's admirers in the College, such as Francis Glisson, Thomas Wharton, George Ent, and others conducted anatomical and pathological researches in the mid-seventeenth century, often in collaboration.

The preface to *A treatise of the rickets*, for example, written by Francis Glisson and first published in Latin in 1650 explained that the book was the result of five years of collaborative research. It was based mainly on the work of Glisson, George Bate and Assuerus Regemorter, but drawing on contributions by a group of eight Fellows. Walter Charleton also praised the spirit of scientific enquiry in the College during the Commonwealth period – the mid-seventeenth century.

Francis Glisson (1597–1677). Oils on canvas, artist unknown, c.1670.

In the College's official lectures [see pages 43–4], and more recently its symposia, Fellows have often reported the results of their investigations into physiological, diagnostic, therapeutic and epidemiological problems, mainly carried out on wards and in laboratories at their places of work.

The College, itself, was not a sponsor of research until the establishment in 1977 of the Medical Services Study Group, later called the Research Unit and now named the Clinical Effectiveness and Evaluation Unit (CEEU). Its original purpose was 'to advance medical knowledge and improve medical care mainly by the collaborative research of its Fellows and Members' under the direction of former President, Sir Cyril Clarke.

Among Sir Cyril's important contributions was his investigation with a British Thoracic Association Group in 1979 of asthma deaths in two regions. This was one of the first studies demonstrating that in young patients dying of an acute condition there are missed opportunities for medical intervention in a significant number of patients – in this instance about two-thirds of cases. This was a seminal study in leading to the development of medical audit during the 1980s, which in turn has developed into the wider remit of clinical governance.

Thomas Wharton (1614–73). Oils on canvas, artist unknown, c.1650.

Under Dr Anthony Hopkins from 1988 to his sudden death in 1997 the unit became a leading centre for clinical audit research, producing under his joint authorship or editorship guidelines on topics such as epilepsy, seizures, angina and care of the elderly. The CEEU now aims to facilitate simple, clear, evidence-based guidelines, to devise and validate measurement tools for assessing best practice, and to devise and validate clinical outcome indicators of the management of patient care. A key feature of a College Unit derives from the collective enthusiasm of Fellows participating in its projects, which ensures that theory can be translated into better care for patients.

Title page of Galen's De sanitate tuenda, *translated by Thomas Linacre, 1517.*

The 1618 Pharmacopoeia. Below: *title page of the first issue;* bottom: *title page of the second issue.*

Galen, Paracelsus and the Development of the *Pharmacopoeia*

The idea and benefits of a standard listing of medicines had been around since the twelfth century and several pharmacopoeias were produced on the Continent during the sixteenth century. The compilation by the College of a pharmacopoeia, to be adopted by all the apothecaries in England, was first mooted in 1585, but nothing concrete happened until the writing of the different sections was assigned to individual Fellows in 1589. And the project stalled five years later even though a second committee was appointed in December 1594 to examine the work already done.

At that time, the use of chemical medicines, introduced by Paracelsus (1493–1541), was still novel and controversial. Nevertheless, the College appointed a subcommittee to report on extracts, salts, *chemica* and *metallica*. This was a departure from any previous pharmacopoeia and the lack of any tangible result from the College's deliberations may be attributed to disagreements between the supporters of traditional Galenical medicine and the Paracelsians.

The pharmacopoeia working party included physicians who had spent a period of their medical training studying at one of the Continental universities known to be sympathetic to Paracelsian ideas, such as Basle and Nantes. Notable among them were Thomas Muffet (1553–1604), who had published books on both chemical and Hippocratic medicine; and Henry Atkins, later to be elected President six times.

In June 1614 Dr Atkins, by then one of the physicians to King James I, gave an oral report to the Fellows on his discussion with the king about the possibility of the apothecaries separating from the Grocers' Company. A majority, believing this would be advantageous to the College and give them more control over the apothecaries, declared themselves in favour.

At the same time a new committee was appointed to plan a 'common dispensatory', based on the published pharmacopoeial literature and work already undertaken by the College. Among the Fellows added to the committee in September 1616 was Sir Theodore de Mayerne [see pages 126–7], who like Muffet was willing to try the new medicines without rejecting what had not been proved useless in the old. Mayerne had already been involved in further discussions with the king on the apothecaries' charter when he was a royal physician but not yet a Fellow, as reported by President Atkins in February 1615.

Atkins reminded the Fellows that they were on oath not to criticise College decisions. At this point Sir William Paddy, who clearly believed that Dr Atkins was being high-handed in pressing this matter on his own account, protested that this was wrong as questions concerning the apothecaries and the City were not internal affairs of the College. The final arrangements for publication of the *Pharmacopoeia* were made on 30 March 1618 – the writing of the dedication to the king (by Mayerne) and the preface, which in the book is dated 7 May 1618.

Although the new chemical medicines are included, the preface is concili-atory to the older school in stressing the auxiliary part they play in the art of healing. This first version was a plain formulary and included only the most common and useful prescriptions, omitting any discussion of the efficacy of the medicines.

However, it was withdrawn and the reason stated in the epilogue to the second issue (that the printer had produced it before it was fully prepared and it was full of errors) probably covers up a more profound disagreement about the form that such a work should take.

The second version is much longer, listing many more simples and compounds and including discussions of the uses of the medicines. It includes the royal proclamation ordering all apothecaries in England to make up medicines according to the formulae prescribed within, which had previ-ously appeared in some copies of the first issue.

The preface of this second issue is dated 7 December 1618, by which time Sir William Paddy had succeeded Atkins as President. This is sometimes given as the date of publication, although the *Annals* record that on the following 13 January the Fellows debated the merits of two rival versions of the epilogue, written respectively by Atkins and Paddy, without saying how the question was resolved.

The College published revisions in 1650, 1677 and 1719 (there were gener-ally several 'editions' or reprints of each edition), but changes were only minor until the 1746 edition, when there was a serious attempt at bringing the contents up to date. Despite the influence of William Heberden the elder even before he became a Fellow [see page 148], the old formulae that had acquired numerous accretions over the centuries were still there in all their glory. For example, Theriac was listed with 61 ingredients and the related Mithridatum with 45, but the writing was on the wall for the kind of polyphar-macy they represented. They were deleted from the 1788 revision, which constituted a further stage in the application of recent scientific knowledge.

Credit should be given to Sir George Baker, the President under whom this, the sixth edition, was produced, and who was one of the more perceptive Presidents of the eighteenth century. The 1746 edition also dropped the explanations of the uses of the medicines, on the grounds that a pharma-copoeia is not 'a regular treatise on the art of pharmacy, but only a register of the medicines, the apothecary is to be furnished with.' This was in fact a return to the principles of the very first issue of May 1618, although the authors were probably not aware of it.

When the next edition was published in 1809 a standing committee was formed, which was to meet at least twice a year to scrutinise any formulae about which doubts were raised and any new medicines that might be recom-mended. In 1813 a motion was put to Comitia that the possibility of an imperial British pharmacopoeia be considered but not carried. The Colleges in Edinburgh and Dublin were each producing their own, though by this time doctors from all parts of Britain were practising in every region of the islands and the Empire.

Sir George Baker (1722–1809). Oils on canvas by Ozias Humphrey, 1794. Baker was nine times elected President between 1785 and 1795. A Devonian, he is best known for his demonstration that the 'Devonshire colic' was lead poisoning caused by the use of lead to line the cider presses.

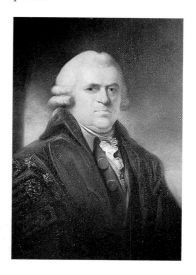

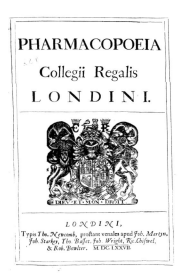

*The 1677 edition of the
Pharmacopoeia.*

*The 1618 Pharmacopoeia: the
king's endorsement of the
publication's authority.*

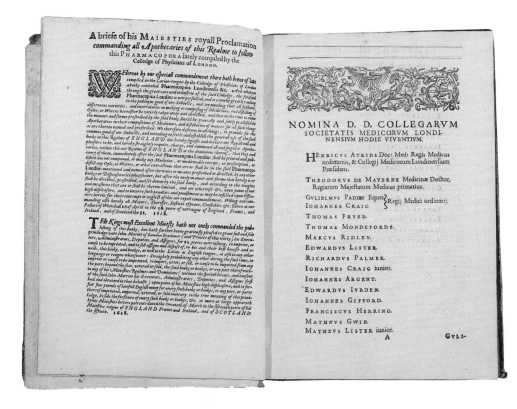

*The 1746 edition of the
Pharmacopoeia – the title
spread (right) and an extract
pertaining to theriac treatments (below).*

The 1824 edition had hardly any changes from the previous one. Dr John Ayrton Paris, a junior member of the committee that produced it and the first College lecturer on materia medica in 1826, recommended the introduction of such new drugs as morphia, iodine and quinine but he was overruled. The ninth edition of 1836, however, over which Dr Paris, among others, took considerable trouble, was much more substantially overhauled. Help with the chemistry was provided by Richard Philips FRS, who also provided an English translation. (All the editions of the College's *Pharmacopoeia Londinensis* were in Latin, although there were also a number of both official and unauthorised English translations and commentaries over the years.)

The idea of an Imperial pharmacopoeia or even a British pharmacopoeia was raised again but the Dublin College rejected it. The tenth edition of 1851

An examination candidate undergoing a viva *examination. Rowlandson and Pugin, 1808 [see page 46].*

The 1851 edition of the Pharmacopoeia.

was the last, as the Medical Act of 1858 gave the responsibility of producing the *British pharmacopoeia* to the new body that the Act established, the General Medical Council. Until that time the College had believed that it was incumbent upon it to undertake this standing national responsibility.

Standards and Guidelines

The setting of standards was seen from the beginning as an essential part of the College's purpose, but it first became involved in the promulgation of guidelines in the early seventeenth century when it published its register of drug formulae, the *London Pharmacopoeia* [see pages 48–52]. Just when this responsibility was being transferred to the General Medical Council in the mid-nineteenth century another kind of reference list was seen to be required.

The Registrar-General began producing annual statistics in 1839, which from the start included causes of death, thanks to a suggestion by the College's own Registrar, Dr Francis Hawkins. For these figures to make sense terminology needed to be standardised and in 1857 the Epidemiological Society asked the College to undertake the compilation of a nomenclature of diseases. The College promptly set up a nomenclature committee, but it was diverted from serious work on the project until 1862 by the constitutional changes it was making in the aftermath of the 1858 Medical Act.

As well as the College, members of the committee included representatives of the Royal College of Surgeons of England, the medical departments of the Army, Navy and the India Office, the Registrar-General of England and the Local Government Board (which was responsible for the nation's health at the time). Other individuals were co-opted for their special medical, statistical or linguistic expertise. Scotland and Ireland were represented from 1862 by the secretaries of their respective Registrar-generals' offices, but their Colleges of Physicians were not specifically involved until the fourth edition of 1906.

The Nomenclature of diseases first appeared in 1869 and listed English terms for diseases with their Latin, French, German and Italian equivalents. Thus it aimed to be more than a parochial list for anglophone doctors (although it was initially given a cool reception in Scotland) and had some influence on the International Statistical Institute's *International list of causes of death*, drawn up in 1899.

Some 20,000 copies of the *Nomenclature* were distributed to medical practitioners in the UK at the government's expense. Even so, there were complaints that doctors were using inconsistent terminology on death certificates, a problem that was still worrying Sir Cyril Clarke as director of the Medical Services Study Group a century later. The main fault of the first edition was thought to be the fact that it was based on morbid anatomy, often unknown especially when the patient recovered, rather than the clinical manifestations of disease. Nevertheless, it proved extremely useful when the notification of infectious diseases was introduced following the Act of Parliament of 1889.

The second edition of 1884 included input from America. It was already in use there as the basis for analysing the world's medical literature for *Index medicus*, which began in 1879. From the early twentieth century the *International list* was increasingly used for death certification on the grounds that getting deaths reported everywhere in the same terms was more important than having an absolutely correct classification.

The Nomenclature of diseases remained the standard manual of nosology until the College decided that its eighth edition of 1960 should be its last. By then it was clear that the *Manual of the international statistical classification of diseases, injuries and causes of death* produced by the World Health Organization was gaining worldwide acceptance.

During the 1940s committees were formed to address questions of standards in several areas of medical and social concern, beginning in 1942 with a memorandum drawn up at the request of the Ministry of Health on the design of dwelling houses. Reports were issued on education, training and the organisation of services in industrial medicine, child health and welfare services and a variety of medical specialties. This trend continued through the 1950s, 1960s and 1970s.

In 1969 the College produced its first short report on the ethics of clinical investigations, with two more in the 1970s. Its *Guidelines on the practice of ethics committees in medical research involving human subjects*, are now widely referred to (3rd edition, 1996). Both the supervising Committee on Ethical Issues in Medicine and the working party that drafted the guidelines included lay members. The formation of the Medical Services Study Group in 1977 (now the Clinical Evaluation and Effectiveness Unit) [see page 47] increased the rate at which standards and guidelines were produced, although reports on quality and effectiveness have continued to emanate also from College committees and working parties. Several reports on the standards of care of the elderly and the care of patients after stroke might be noted. An increasing feature has been the input of non-College expertise, from both medical and patients' organisations. It is obviously appropriate, for example, when considering problems associated with epilepsy to involve the Institute of Neurology and the National Society for Epilepsy (report published in 1997).

The CEEU also accepts commissions for work from a variety of organisations including the National Institute for Clinical Excellence (NICE) and works with the NHS Information Authority and the National Clinical Governance Support Team on projects that are mostly linked to the national priorities as set out by the government.

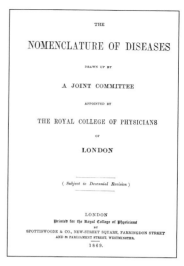

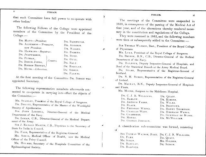

The Nomenclature of diseases: top: *title page;* middle: *a list of committee members;* above: *lists of diseases in the full range of languages.*

College Publications

It was not until the 1960s that the College produced regular publications. There had been, however, a flourish of activity in the eighteenth century, curiously connected with Dr Samuel Johnson.

One of his young friends was Edmund Barker who succeeded George Edwards as Bedell in 1760 [see pages 82–4]. Barker, an MD of Leyden, gave up medicine to use his linguistic talents, turning the Latin of Heister's *Compendium of physic* into English, and Edwards' *Gleanings of natural history* into French. The two Fellows concerned in this development were Mark Akenside who featured in Johnson's *Lives of the poets* and Thomas Lawrence who was Johnson's physician. In 1766 the College published the works of William Harvey with a preface by Akenside and a biography by Lawrence, indexed and seen through the press by Barker. Every Fellow was given a copy, but Licentiates had to pay. In the same year the College, using the same triumvirate and William Heberden the elder, decided to publish its *Medical Transactions* based on papers read at special meetings. The Licentiates, already in dispute with the College, refused to submit papers. However the first volume of the *Transactions* appeared in 1768, reprinted in 1772 and 1785. Barker resigned as Bedell in 1771 but the next volume was published in 1772, reprinted in 1786. Despite the initial success, support withered over the years with sporadic publication in 1785, 1813, 1815 and lastly 1820.

Two centuries later the College abandoned its customary reticence to plunge into the realm of public health by publishing in 1962 its report *Smoking and health* [see pages 57–9]. Two years later the College was in Regent's Park contemplating its educational role. The new *Advanced Medicine Conference* was published annually from 1965.

At the same time Dr R. R. (Dick) Bomford conceived the idea of a quarterly College Journal of general interest to Fellows and for the new Collegiate Membership. Supported by Sir Theodore Fox, former editor of *The Lancet*, Bomford overcame considerable opposition within the College to launch the first issue of the *Journal of the Royal College of Physicians of London* in October 1966. Each issue was accompanied by the *College Commentary* giving news and views of its officers, with circulation restricted to Fellows only. The *Journal* editor, personally appointed by the President, had the freedom to compile an independent journal. If it failed, the College could disclaim responsibility for its contents and the President accept the editor's resignation. Those were the days of only 1000 Fellows, of hot-metal printing and cowgum paste-ups. Production of the *Journal* was in the hands of publishers, initially Pitman. Over the years the *Journal* became established and later published free-standing reports of College working parties.

The 1980s saw a rising tempo of change. The number of Fellows increased and College activities expanded. A technological revolution swept through publishing and printing. In 1986 Diana Beaven came from the world of publishing to manage a College publication department designed to integrate all aspects of the field. A year later the *Journal* dispensed with its publisher and dealt directly with its printers.

In 1988 the College made the *Journal* editor (then Robert Mahler) an officer of the College and the Research Unit initiated a continuing series of reports and guidelines on medical audit. Desktop publishing became a technical possibility. The publication department added expert staff but was not fully equipped for complete in-house publishing until 1993. The invaluable Continuing Medical Education section was added to the *Journal* by David Kerr in l997 and is now the backbone of the publication.

In 1994 the *Journal* changed to a bi-monthly frequency, with some 600 pages each year, catering for 10,000 Fellows. It is now also published electronically by OVID and on the College website. Peter Watkins, editor, has just changed the title to *Clinical Medicine*. Meanwhile the publications department with 130 titles under its belt is a profitable success.

Munk's Roll

'Munk's Roll' is the name by which the *Lives of the Fellows of the Royal College of Physicians of London* is generally known. Entries are now written immediately after the death of the subjects by friends or colleagues, and published on the College website. But the first three volumes of *The Roll of the Royal College of Physicians of London* were written by William Munk and consisted of biographical sketches of all Fellows, Candidates, Licentiates and Extra-Licentiates up to 1825.

William Munk was born in 1816 in Battle, Sussex, of a Devonian family, the son of an ironmonger. He studied medicine at University College, London, but graduated from the University of Leyden in Holland. He became a Fellow in 1854 – late enough to avoid falling foul of the College rule that had until 1835 restricted the Fellowship to graduates of Oxford or Cambridge.

The Roll was first published in two volumes in 1861, and it is now known from its three-volume second edition of 1878, to which were added chapters on various aspects of College history and lists of office holders and lecturers. Munk undertook to research the biographies initially, he explained, 'with the hope of supplying a want I had myself experienced'. As he completed each section he deposited it in the library for the use of Fellows and was elected Harveian librarian in 1857, serving until his death in 1898.

As he was writing for private consumption he had not kept careful notes of all his sources and hesitated to allow the College to publish his work. But he hoped that it would 'not prove devoid of interest to those who have the welfare of the medical profession at heart, and are desirous of obtaining more information than has hitherto been obtainable concerning that venerable institution, The Royal College of Physicians of London.'

William Munk (1816–98). Photograph by Moira and Haigh, 1864.

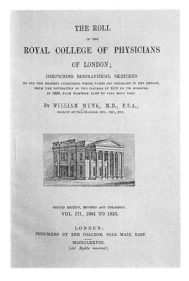

Munk's Roll.
Top: *volumes 1–9;*
above: *the title page of*
volume 3.

Aneurin Bevan in 1950.

Many of the errors in it that have now come to light are due to the limited amount of research he conducted beyond the sources available to him in the College. He got the two John Pecheys – the extra-Licentiate of 1683 and the Licentiate of 1684, translator into English of Thomas Sydenham's works – completely confused, as George Peachey showed in 1918. But his principal source was the College *Annals*, which he had read right through. The bulk of the data he found there is transcribed accurately in *The Roll* – mistakes are more often found in his lists at the end of volume 3 than in the body of the work.

Readers should realise that he did not reveal everything he knew about College affairs, especially where the College and its Licentiates were concerned. For example ten entries in the *Annals* of 1609–10 tell of the appearances before the Censors' board of Licentiate Stephen Bredwell and of his surly attitude towards the President, but Munk gave no hint of this altercation.

He noted the admission as a Licentiate in 1646 of Gerard Boet MD Leyden, but said nothing about the other twenty-eight entries in the *Annals*, beginning in 1630, recording the College's prosecutions of Boet for illegal practice and his attempts to get himself examined.

And he had a notion of a past medical golden age, as his response to a request in 1884 for information about a more recent Fellow shows: 'I take little interest in the present degenerate race of physicians ... my Memoranda are limited almost exclusively to physicians who joined the College in the old and regular way before 1825.' This was despite the fact that both his medical education (not Oxford or Cambridge) and his religion (a convert to Roman Catholicism in 1842) would have rendered him ineligible for the Fellowship in 'the old and regular way'.

But as Sir George Clark wrote: 'Dr Munk's work contains much material that cannot be found elsewhere and is indispensable to any student of the history of the College.'

The College and the NHS

The College played an active role in public health matters in the seventeenth century but by the early nineteenth century its involvement had declined to the extent that when Asiatic cholera threatened in 1831 the College was omitted from the Board of Health set up by the Privy Council to deal with the problem. It was considered that the College represented a small body of practitioners who spent little time on public matters and lacked the administrative structure to gather information quickly and make prompt recommendations.

Early in the twentieth century there was a growing body of public and medical opinion that the country needed a national, comprehensive health service, but effective planning did not begin until the landslide victory for Labour in the summer of 1945. Within three months, the shape of the proposed Health Service was firmly set under the leadership of the charismatic

Aneurin Bevan. The profession quickly realised the importance of establishing a good relationship with him. For the College, the President, Lord Moran, seized the initiative. The profession was divided with the British Medical Association (BMA) implacably opposed, the surgeons more in favour, and the College strongly so. Comitia in May 1946 approved by 88 votes to 13 a motion embodying comprehensive support for the National Health Service bill, a turning point in the debate. The difficulties, however, were not over. At the end of 1946, when Bevan came to discuss with the profession the details under which the service would operate, 55 per cent of the members of the BMA voted against negotiating, but the College Council, in a decision which was approved by Comitia, voted unanimously to do so. The Presidents of the Royal Colleges of Physicians, Surgeons and Obstetricians and Gynaecologists met Bevan and then wrote to the *British Medical Journal* setting out the contentious points. Bevan, as previously agreed, replied and was sufficiently encouraging for negotiations to begin.

In December 1947 the BMA again raised major difficulties, its greatest anxiety being that a whole-time salaried service for general practitioners might be brought in by regulation. In February 1948 the membership voted 8 to 1 against accepting service under the Act. Moran went to see Bevan on 10 March and suggested that what was needed was an amending Act to lay down that a whole-time service would not be introduced without the sanction of Parliament. Bevan agreed and proposed that once again the three Presidents should write, asking for such a bill.

A new problem now arose. The Presidential Election was due on 22 March. Lord Horder, who was deeply opposed to the NHS, was a powerful rival. If he were elected, it was highly unlikely that he would sign the letter. But after tense voting Moran won by 6 votes.

The plan went ahead. The Presidents signed and on 7 April Bevan made his conciliatory statement in the House of Commons. Another BMA plebiscite showed that 8,000 GPs had changed their minds and were in favour of entering the National Health Service. In May the BMA withdrew its objections and the National Health Service started on the 'Appointed Day' 5 July 1948. The College had re-established itself as a force in public affairs.

Correspondence between Moran and Bevan, 1948.

Smoking and Public Health

The College's involvement in the 1960s in raising smoking as an issue of public concern was a highly significant point in its history and in post-war health policy. It placed the College for the first time at the centre of the polit-ical process and paved the way for the College to make pronouncements about, and respond to, major health issues in the future.

The 1962 report *Smoking and health* was a vivid document and conveyed the epidemiological case to both the general public and to policy makers.

A 1950s advertisement for cigarettes, claiming medical approval of the product.

But the genesis of the College's involvement was tortuous. In 1956, the gastroenterologist Francis Avery Jones who worked at the Central Middlesex Hospital, a centre of anti-smoking sentiment, suggested to Sir Russell Brain, then President of the College, that the College should make a statement on the matter. Avery Jones suggested that it should be referred to the College's Social and Preventive Medicine Committee.

Brain, however, saw no reason to do this. His justification for this reflected the standard response at that time. 'The work of Richard Doll and Bradford Hill has received very wide publicity and must be known, I should imagine, to every doctor in the country, so it is difficult to see that the College could add anything to the knowledge of the existing facts. If we go beyond facts, to the question of the giving of advice to the public as to what action they should take in the light of the facts, I doubt very much whether that should be a function of the College.'

Matters changed when Robert Platt was elected President of the College in 1957 in succession to Brain. Sir George Godber, then deputy chief medical officer in the Ministry of Health, was frustrated by attitudes in the Ministry towards smoking at the time. There was little activity at ministerial level and the Standing Advisory Committee on Cancer, together with the Central Health Services Council, were unwilling, for various reasons, to do anything either.

Godber worked with Charles Fletcher, first director of the Medical Research Council's pneumoconiosis research unit in Cardiff, and at this time working as a respiratory physician in the department of medicine at Hammersmith Hospital, to take the issue through the College. This was also a way of exerting pressure on Sir John Charles, the chief medical officer, who would only react himself if there was external concern. Platt readily agreed to take it up. Smoking fitted well with his 'modernising' agenda for the 'stuffy College' that he had taken over.

The committee on smoking and air pollution, with Fletcher as its secretary, began its work in 1959. Its initial focus was to educate doctors, but its work took new directions both for public health and for the College. The committee decided to leave air pollution out of its consideration in favour of an exclusive focus on smoking and lung cancer and also agreed that the report should have much wider publicity and circulation than the usual College documents. The aim was to inform and advise the public and to suggest lines of action to government as well.

In order to achieve these aims, the College appointed a professional public relations person to manage the report's launch, which was marked by the College's first ever press conference. The report was an unusual publishing success for the College. It sold 33,000 copies by the autumn of 1963 in the UK and over 50,000 in the US.

The UK government appointed a Cabinet committee to consider the College's report and it was also instrumental in stimulating the American Surgeon General's 1964 report on smoking.

The report's publication in the UK marked a change in public health from consideration of population issues to a focus on an individual's responsibility, advice to the public on the health action they should take and lifestyle considerations they should make. For medicine and public health, it marked the beginning of attempts to improve a public understanding of science (in this case chronic disease epidemiology) and gave the College a role in advising government on smoking and other aspects of health policy.

Within the College and the medical profession, it was part of a 'modernising' thrust, which placed the College in a more central role in moves to reform medical education. All this was very different from the inward-looking stance taken in the Brain years. Medicine, public health and the College had entered a new era.

The 1971 report *Smoking and health now* created a similar public stir. Its content marked the beginnings of a changed and politically radical agenda for anti-smoking. The report still placed stress on less hazardous smoking, either through switching to pipes and cigars, filter tips for cigarettes, warning labels on packets, and the development of a 'safer cigarette'. But it also laid emphasis on differential taxation as a means to encourage less harmful smoking and called for an official enquiry to be carried out into the economic consequences of a decrease in smoking. The government did in fact carry out this enquiry, as well as re-establishing the Cabinet committee on smoking, but the results were never officially published. The publication of the College report was once more the occasion for significant developments in the relationship between the public, the College and the medical profession.

The formation of the pressure group ASH, Action on Smoking and Health, in 1971 carried forward the anti-smoking cause. The initiative came from the College but ASH emerged as a pressure group mainly funded by the Department of Health – a relationship that was characteristic of other pressure groups and established bodies in the 1970s.

Further reports in 1977, 1983, 1992 and 2000 have continued the College's involvement in smoking policy, latterly focusing on more specific issues such as smoking and the young or nicotine addiction. None has had quite the impact of the first two reports. The later publications have appeared when the acceptability of smoking is waning and have contributed to that trend, rather than initiating it, as did the 1962 and 1971 reports.

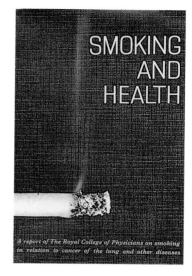

The first report Smoking and health, *published in 1962.*

3

College Premises
and Precincts

It says much for the stability and status of the College that is has been based at only five separate premises in over 480 years. Its founder, Thomas Linacre, was foremost among scholars but could not provide the endowments that enriched ancient colleges at Oxford and Cambridge, for example. Nevertheless, he gave the front portion of his own house over to the College in 1518. This provided one room as a meeting place and another as a library stocked with his own books. It was enough for the handful of Fellows at the time.

The house was in Knightrider Street, just south of St Paul's Cathedral. It was called the Stone House to distinguish it from the timber buildings common in the City at the time, but it was small and far from grand. On his death in 1524 Linacre left the Stone House to the College and early in the 1580s a theatre

Two plans showing the College properties in Knightrider Street, Amen Corner and Warwick Lane.
Right: *a street plan – Amen Corner is the lower highlighted site.*
Far right: *a ground plan showing the house and gardens of the College, mid-1600s.*

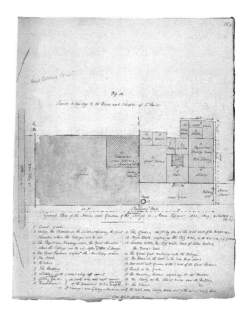

was added for the lectures on anatomy [see page 40]. In 1587 the College rented a nearby garden to be tended by John Gerard, famous for his *Herball*.

After the turn of the seventeenth century the increasing Fellowship needed larger premises, and money to pay for them. Contributions came from Lady Arabella Stuart and her aunt, the Countess of Shrewsbury – generous gifts considering both women were prisoners in the Tower. Dr Gwinne, the College Registrar, was physician to the Tower and may have influenced them.

However the College could not raise enough money to purchase a house, let alone build one. So a property at Amen Corner, Paternoster Row, was leased from St Paul's. This was a large house west of the cathedral and was probably modified to give a spacious meeting room and library. There were also two rooms for anatomy and accommodation for a resident Fellow to guard the building and keep the library. There was no official opening ceremony, the College quietly starting to use its new home in August 1614.

During the Civil War, Parliament confiscated all church lands to raise money from their sale. That the College did not lose Amen Corner was thanks to the generosity of Dr Baldwin Hamey who bought the lease and later gave it to the College. As the Commonwealth settled down it was announced in 1651 that the College had found a donor to fund a new library and museum. Everybody knew that the donor was Dr William Harvey but his name was not mentioned officially. Harvey had hastened to the king's side when war broke out and so was declared a malignant by Parliament and for many years banned from visiting the College he loved. When the library had been built it was opened in 1654 with Harvey present amid much rejoicing. According to John Aubrey it was a noble building of Roman architecture with a great parlour below for meetings of the Fellows and with the library above.

The College prospered during the Commonwealth, providing three physicians for Cromwell. With the restoration of the monarchy it was eager to gain the king's favour and Charles II obliged with a visit.

The College building at Amen Corner was destroyed on the fourth day of the Great Fire (1666). Dr Merrett, the resident Fellow, managed to save the College insignia and *Annals*, a carpet and some 100 books from the library. His own accommodation and all his possessions were lost. He was the hero of the hour, making amends for leaving the College unguarded during the Great Plague of the previous year when all the College cash and silver were stolen.

The Fellows quickly resumed College business, meeting in each other's houses. Finding new premises was high on the agenda but took years to achieve. Meanwhile there was the black farce of the College versus Merrett. As the library had been destroyed in the fire, the College refused to pay Merrett as its keeper. In retaliation, Merrett refused to give up what he had rescued and the issue ended in court. The College got back its treasures and Merrett was expelled: it was symptomatic of an inglorious period in the College history.

Rebuilding on the Amen Corner site was impossible because no agreement on a new lease could be gained from St Paul's which had its own problems. Fellows were asked for money and College fines were collected rather than forgotten.

After several false starts a site in nearby Warwick Lane was purchased in 1669 from Mr Hollier, surgeon-lithotomist to the hospitals of St Bartholomew

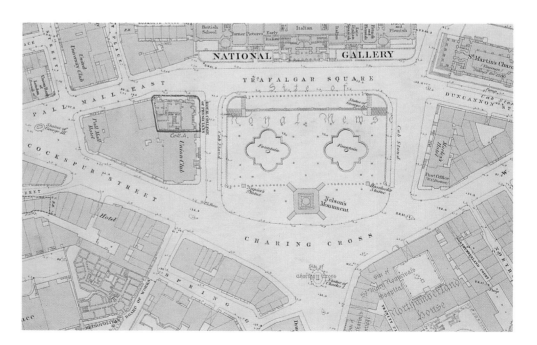

A plan showing the Pall Mall East site, highlighted in red.

62

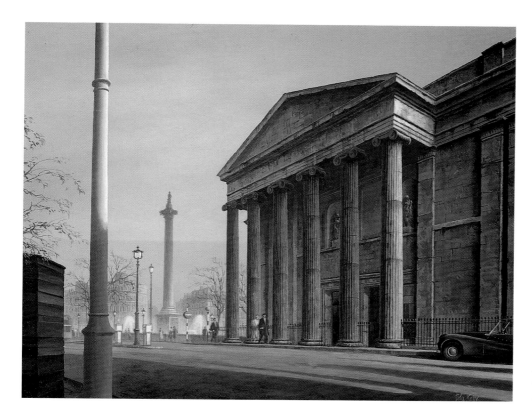

The Royal College of Physicians, Pall Mall East. Oils on board, by Felix Kelly, 1960.

Trafalgar Square, viewed from the College building in Pall Mall East. Oils on board, by Felix Kelly, 1964.

Sir John Cutler. This statue was mounted on the inner wall of the Cutlerian anatomy theatre, facing the courtyard, in 1680.

Below: *an engraving of the College published in 1828. Below right: the College photographed in 1876, after the three statues were installed.*

and St Thomas and remover of Pepys's bladder stone. The new building was designed by Robert Hooke, the polymath secretary to the Royal Society, who surveyed London after the fire together with Christopher Wren. The new building had a central courtyard with the public rooms facing the gateway. The courtyard was flanked by wings on either side that provided accommodation for a Fellow, the Bedell and the College chemist. Other apartments were available to let.

The building of the wings was organised and paid for by Sir George Ent, PRCP 1670–6, with the rented rooms providing a source of income. On the first floor of the public rooms was the magnificent long gallery panelled in Spanish oak at Hamey's expense. A last-minute gift came in 1674 when the rich Sir John Cutler said he would build a theatre over the gateway. The builders were still at work when the College quietly started business and held the Comitia there in 1675.

Initially, there was no provision for a library as there were no books to fill one. But in 1680 the Fellows were told that the Marquis of Dorchester's magnificent library was to be donated to them. Christopher Wren was asked to make the changes needed in the new building to accommodate such a treasure.

For the first time the College had built and owned its premises. The building was much larger than the College needed but very elegant. It attracted a stream of visitors, each advised to give three pence to whomever showed them round.

The only problem was the environs of Warwick Lane. John Evelyn wrote, 'Tis pitty this Colledge is built so neere new-gate Prison and in so obscure an hole.'

The peace of the Warwick Lane building was undisturbed for nearly a century. Then, on 24 September 1767 the Licentiates who had a grudge against the College stormed Comitia breaking the gates and smashing many windows in the process [see page 36]. London was agog at the news of professional men behaving so badly.

By the end of the eighteenth century the westward drift of physicians and their patients was making Warwick Lane an inconvenient place for the

College to be. In 1799 it was proposed that the College look for a new building in the West End. As the original jurisdiction of the College was confined to the City of London a parliamentary Bill was needed to allow it to operate in the City of Westminster.

The necessary Bill was passed in 1814, the heyday of John Nash's architectural sweep from the Mall to Regent's Park. The College refused a site in the new Regent's Street because it was leasehold. Then Nash offered a site in Pall Mall East as he began to develop that area. He even presented the College with detailed drawings of a building in 1816. The site was accepted but work on it was delayed while, once more, the College looked for funds.

In the end the Nash design was rejected and the architect of the Pall Mall East home was Robert Smirke whose classical design was severe 'almost to the point of dullness' – exactly suiting the personality of the President, Sir Henry Halford. As PRCP from 1820 to 1844 he was a very superior person, a royal physician with a huge practice. He convinced society that physicians were men of importance and standing. So much so that when the building was opened with much ceremony in 1825 the guests were headed by five princes, five dukes, including Wellington, 13 peers, the prime minister and Sir Thomas Lawrence who had painted most of their portraits.

Smirke also designed the Union Club so that the east aspect of the Club and the College formed one harmonious building that overlooked Trafalgar Square. The College's imposing entrance portico, with six Ionic columns, was on Pall Mall East. From the entrance hall the staircase, flanked by double Doric columns, rose to split into two, illuminated by windows that, in 1887, were decorated with stained-glass portrayals of the arms of Fellows. At the top of the stairs was the huge library, two storeys high and lit only by skylights. On the ground floor was the dining room that doubled as a lecture theatre. The Censors' room on the first floor was lined with the Spanish oak panels taken from Warwick Lane.

After 50 years of London air the building needed extensive repairs. This was an opportunity to fill the two empty niches on the pediment of the portico and make a third by removing the central window. Statues of Linacre, Harvey and Sydenham were commissioned and installed in 1875. When the College left Pall Mall East nearly 100 years later the statues were found to be so corroded that they were junked in a builder's yard. Personal interests led to their rescue. Two went to Kent, Harvey's to the new William Harvey public house and Sydenham's to a group practice. Linacre's went to a Linacre family living in London.

A century after the brilliant opening of the building the College seemed to fall asleep. The building was more a mausoleum than the headquarters of an active institution. When the young Dr Charles Newman was appointed assistant Registrar in 1933 he found the College to be very small, very grand and very inert. However, he was joined by the redoubtable Miss Cook, the first woman to work in the College, who brought with her the first typewriter to be used there.

The Royal College in Regent's Park, designed by Sir Denys Lasdun.

The main staircase.

Main picture: *the Censors' room from the outside.*
Inset: *the inside of the Censors' room, the heart of the Lasdun building, complete with the panelling in Spanish oak first used in Warwick Lane.*

Above: *a procession makes its way up the staircase.*
Above right and below: *a presentation ceremony in the library.*

The Royal College of Physicians in Regent's Park

Many people interested in the history of the College must ask themselves whether or not the premises in Regent's Park was an inspiration to Presidents and Fellows in the latter part of the twentieth century. And, if so, what part did it play in the development of the College and the direction of its activities.

The site became available because the previous building, Someries House, was extensively bomb-damaged in World War II. Although the adjacent Nash Terraces had to be restored, the Crown Estate Commissioners offered the Someries House site in 1958 and (Sir) Denys Lasdun was appointed architect in September 1958.

The building was opened in 1964. At last the College had premises designed entirely for its own needs and reflecting its history and aspirations. Lasdun brought to the building a vast array of different influences, but without losing sight of the kernel of the College's activities to maintain standards in the practice and research of medicine and to disseminate its messages to the international medical community through lectures and conferences.

Externally, the building complements the lines and stature of the Nash Terraces, but it also reflects the influence of Le Corbusier and other modernists. Internally and externally, the elements work together at many different levels, both visually and intellectually.

That Lasdun was designing a building for an august medical body was a significant influence. Lasdun himself thought of the building as a living organism: 'It is more a piece of organisation sensitised to its external context and capable of growth and change. It is, therefore, an organism in which the architect is primarily concerned with routes, focal points and the enclosing fabric – an organism, complete and incomplete at the same time.'

And it is known that while he was designing the building Lasdun studied Harvey's diagrams of the circulation of the blood. One architectural writer has commented on the power of this metaphor: 'One may even think of the building as a sort of "body of knowledge" with the research laboratories as the feet, the Censors' room as the heart (complete with panelling in Spanish oak first used in Warwick Lane), the library as the head and the various nodes of the plan as organs.'

Visitors to Regent's Park are struck by a white building with clean lines rising above them as they climb the entrance steps. Inside, there is even a sense as the interior soars above that it is larger than the exterior. The hall serves as a forum and portrait gallery, as well as providing a sweeping square spiral staircase used to great effect on ceremonial occasions, and both the library and the dining hall are two storeys deep.

The main view from College rooms is not the expanse of Regent's Park but to the south over the precinct of St Andrews Place, now home to a number of College departments.

In the 1990s, Lasdun was given the opportunity to extend the building to provide addtional facilities. In a lecture given to the College in 1996 he explained: 'It comprises a meeting room, lecture theatre, dining facilities and displays for the College's silver. It is the realisation of something that was anticipated and made provision for long ago when the new College was first conceived. Placed on the central axis with the Censors' room, the extension now gives overall symmetry to the College.'

And later he said that the meeting room turned out to be one of the three 'entirely satisfactory spaces' of all his work.

Together with St Andrews Place the College was designated as a medical precinct by HM The Queen in June 1986 and the main building was listed Grade I in 1998.

The foot of the main staircase (far left).

4

The Library

Sir Francis Prujean (1593–1666). Oils on canvas attributed to Robert Streeter, 1662(?).

A design for the proposed Musaeum Harveianum, *by John Webb, 1651.*

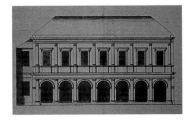

According to College tradition the library began with the gift from the first President, Thomas Linacre, of his own books, at or soon after the foundation of the College. There is no positive record of the fact in the *Annals*, but as only a handful of books are mentioned in his will of 19 June 1524, the bulk must already have been given to the College. Other donations, including some substantial collections like the 680 volumes from the German physician and surgeon, Matthew Holsbosch in 1629, had enlarged the library considerably 100 years later.

In 1571 the books were kept in a chest, but by 1632, when borrowing was permitted if a pledge for twice the value of the book was given to the Censors, they were in bookcases.

On 4 July 1651 President Francis Prujean asked the Fellows: 'If I can procure one, that will build us a Library, and a Repository for Simples and Rarities, such a one as shall be suitable and honorable to the Colledge; will ye assent to have it done, or no?' This request received their unanimous agreement. The designs for the building are dated for the same year, so in all likelihood the money for the project was already promised. The *Annals* do not reveal that William Harvey was the donor until they report his speech at the opening of the building in February 1654. But as the physician and friend of the recently executed monarch, Harvey may have been doubtful about his status in the College under the Commonwealth regime in 1651 and decided to keep a low profile.

His gift to the College of his patrimonial estate of Burmarsh in Kent was intended to endow the library as well as an annual oration and dinner. By the time he presented the trust deed, dated 21 June 1656, the new library had already attracted gifts, including a bequest by the lawyer, John Selden, of 11 medical manuscripts in Arabic and £100 from the Marquis of Dorchester, who was made an honorary Fellow two years later.

The rules of this *Musaeum Harveianum* include a paragraph on book selection policy. 'Besides medical books we consider those to be especially useful and suitable for this Museum, which deal with Geometry, or Geography, or

Cosmography, or Astronomy, or Music, or Optics, or Natural History, Physics or Mechanics, or include Voyages to the more remote regions of the Earth.'

The 1,278 titles of books listed in the catalogue that Dr Christopher Merrett produced in 1660 are mostly of medical or anatomical interest, but nearly all the recommended subjects, and some additional ones, are also represented. The Fellows evidently expected their library to be similar in its coverage to those they had known in their Oxford or Cambridge colleges; there was, of course no university in London at the time.

Unfortunately the Great Fire of London destroyed most of this library in 1666. Merrett, the first Harveian librarian, and the Bedell saved as many as they could – in the region of 100 books, various charters and other treasures – although his efforts ended in dispute. The 1656 library statutes said, 'Let the term of life and of office be the same for the Custodian of this Museum, unless for serious reasons it shall appear otherwise to the College.' Merrett believed that having discharged his duties faithfully he should retain the post (and its £20 per annum honorarium) for life, while the College thought that the loss of virtually its entire library came under the heading of 'serious reasons'.

Merrett held on to the books, the College took him to Chancery to regain possession and won; he took umbrage and ceased to attend Comitia, and the College rescinded his Fellowship in 1681. This was a tragedy both for Merrett and the College. Merrett had been a great defender of the College's rights and privileges in print. A few years after his expulsion alterations were made to the College buildings in order to house the Marquis of Dorchester's books, so that the College could have a library again. Dorchester died in December 1680, but it was not until February 1688 that the books were in place. His library contained some 3,400 volumes (2,101 separate titles), which are kept, as originally agreed, as a separate collection, not incorporated into the general sequence [see pages 73–6, 88].

Thereafter the library grew mainly by donations and bequests by Fellows. Among the more substantial was the bequest of £500 by Richard Hale (d.1728) with which books selected by his nephew, Richard Tyson, were bought. Thomas Crowe (d.1751) left 'such of my printed books as have no English in them and as they have not already in their Library ... or if mine be better copies though they have them already.'

Just a few book purchases are recorded in a separate library account book for the later eighteenth century, but there were evidently some in the College who had an eye on recent developments in medicine. Morgagni's *De sedibus et causis morborum*, published in 1761, was bought for £1 2s. 0d. in 1766; and the only two entries in the financial year 1798–9 were for *Jenner on the Cow Pox* (7s. 6d.) and *Willan on Cutaneous Diseases* (15s.). Most of the books given were of an antiquarian or classical nature, but more than 700 books came from the estate of Thomas Gisborne following his death in 1806, including a large number of comparatively recent works. These were followed in 1823 by the library of Matthew Baillie, a working library of more

Below: two of the library's modern editions given in 2000 by Professor Patrick Lawther.

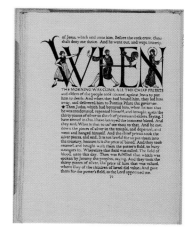

An edition of the King James Gospels, printed and published by the Golden Cockerel Press, 1931, designed and illustrated by Eric Gill.

A double spread of the 1930 edition of the Arabic romance The stealing of the mare, *printed by the Gregynog Press.*

An example of Greek printing in Venice, 1500.

William Munk (1816–98). Oils on canvas by John Collier, 1898.

than 900 volumes, most of which had been published in Baillie's lifetime and around half since the beginning of the nineteenth century.

It is not known exactly when a library committee was constituted – the earliest surviving minutes are dated 1846 – but it met quarterly from the mid-nineteenth century onwards. It is hard to discern what purchase policy it adopted although there were regular subscriptions to English, American, French and German journals by the latter half of the century. Among significant donors of books and manuscripts in the twentieth century are Sir William Osler, David Lloyd Roberts, Evan Bedford [see pages 77–80] and gynaecologists Herbert Ritchie Spencer and Roy Dobbin.

Following the ending of Merrett's tenure, elections to the specific office of Harveian librarian rarely occurred, and the duties were carried out on an *ad hoc* basis for almost two centuries. The former President, Walter Charleton, was appointed less than five months before his death in 1707 at the age of 87, and from 1734 to 1750 Richard Tyson (mentioned above) held the position while, at the same time, also serving successively as Registrar, Treasurer and President. Otherwise general supervision of the library was sometimes assigned to the Registrar, and sometimes to committees composed of various other officers.

In 1857 William Munk was elected Harveian librarian, remaining in office until his death in 1898, and since then there has been a Fellow in this post continuously. At the time of Munk's appointment the College was attempting to run a library of current medicine, but he was chosen because of his interest in the biographies of past Fellows [see page 55]. All holders of the office since then have had a strong interest in the history of medicine.

A committee set up by Edward Browne when he was President in 1708, in addition to several other suggestions including the banning of tobacco smoking in the library, proposed that there should be an 'under library keeper' to be in charge of the day-to-day running of the library. The committee also thought: 'That if hereafter it shall be thought convenient to join this place with that of the Beadle (*sic*) of the College, then the expence of the College hereby will be lessen'd, and by having a Lodging in the College he will be more ready at hand on all occasions.'

In November 1710 the Fellows decided that the Bedell should take charge of the library 'till a Library Keeper can be chose' and the two jobs, though in fact combined for nearly two centuries, remained notionally separate, each with its own chapter in the statutes. Mr Nathan Smith received his first extra £10 'for his care and paynes abt the Library' on 22 December 1711.

Towards the end of the nineteenth century, due to the expansion of the Bedell's secretarial duties, an assistant librarian was appointed and by 1950 the Harveian librarian, Sir Charles Dodds, was insisting that an experienced qualified librarian should be in charge. Under his aegis the policy of medical history with a bias towards biography, plus service to the College departments, was adopted, leaving the provision of current clinical literature to medical schools and other libraries that had already become more substantially involved in that field.

Since then the growing activities of the College have made greater claims on the library and there is now a greater emphasis on health policy, medical education and clinical evaluations. Coverage continues, however, of the history of the College, its Fellows and events and activities involving them. It was in 1970 that the then librarian, Leonard Payne, took stock of the value and extent of the archives and manuscripts and persuaded the College that a qualified archivist was needed. The burgeoning quantity of documents in the College led to the establishment of a records management programme in 1993.

The Dorchester Library

Henry Pierrepont (1606–80), Viscount Newark, succeeded his father as Earl of Kingston-upon-Hull in 1643 and was made 1st Marquis of Dorchester in 1645. Although he sat in the Oxford Parliament he did not actually fight for the king, and in November 1646 Parliament allowed him to pay a fine of £7,467, estimated to be one-tenth of the value of his estate.

Thereafter he was left in peace to follow his interest in scholarship. He is said to have read for 10 or 12 hours a day, becoming knowledgeable about many subjects including medicine, reputedly becoming the best unqualified practitioner in England at the time.

It was probably his personal physician, Edward Browne, Fellow and later President of the College, who persuaded the Marquis to leave his books to the College, to replace the library it had lost in the fire of London. Correspondence between Browne and his father, Sir Thomas Browne (of *Religio medici* fame) as well as some cryptic entries in the *Annals* in 1680 indicate that the gift or bequest was anticipated. The books are not mentioned specifically in the Marquis's will but were probably left in trust to his daughter, Lady Grace Pierrepont, to be passed on to the College.

Henry Pierrepont, 1st Marquis of Dorchester (1606–80). Oils on canvas, artist unknown, 1691.

The *Annals* suggest that the College originally intended to build an extension in the garden to house the Dorchester library, but could not get planning permission from the Corporation of London. Eventually the Fellows decided that they must make alterations within the existing building, for which they called in Sir Christopher Wren, and at last in February 1688 they invited Lady Grace to view the books in place. (Sir George Clark located the library incorrectly in the garden in the first volume of the official College history published in 1964.)

According to a future President of the College, Charles Goodall, the Marquis's library was 'perhaps the best Library for Physique, Mathematique, Civile Law, and Philology in any private hand in this Nation for a choyce collection of books, to the value of above £4,000.'

The collection came with a manuscript catalogue compiled in 1664, divided into four categories. *Libri mathematici* included 825 titles covering astronomy,

73

*John Dee
(1527–1608).
Stipple engraving by
R. Cooper.*

Geoffrey Chaucer. The
Canterbury Tales. *c.1440–50.
Below:* the Prologue; *below
right: a double spread.*

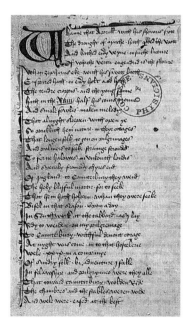

An extract from The Canterbury
Tales *about the 'Doctor of Physik'.*

architecture, music, navigation and military science; *Libri juris civilis* included 508 titles of canon law; *Libri medici* included 192 titles of natural history; and *Libri philologici* included 576 titles of theology, philosophy, classics, history, politics, poetry and fiction. There were also over 100 books formerly owned by the Elizabethan mathematician, alchemist and astrologer, John Dee. Several of these contain evidence which shows that a subsequent owner, Sir Nicholas Saunder, was a thief or a receiver of books stolen during Dee's absence abroad in the 1580s.

Among rarities in the collection is the illuminated manuscript of the mid-thirteenth-century Wilton Psalter [see page 88] and a mid-fifteenth-century manuscript of Chaucer's *Canterbury Tales*. There are 20 books printed in or before the year 1500, including the 1476 edition of Plutarch's *Lives* printed in Venice by Nicolas Jenson and *L'art et instruction de bien dancer* (c.1490), the only surviving copy of the first printed book on the art of dancing. There is also the volume on which William Caxton collaborated with Colard Mansion in Bruges before introducing the art of printing to England: Raoul Lefevre's *The recuyell of the historyes of Troye*.

Geoffrey Chaucer. The Canterbury Tales. c.1440–50 (MS).

This manuscript was probably written in the workshops founded by John Shirley to meet the popular demand for the works of Chaucer. He set up a lending library for those who could not afford to buy books. Written at speed, it is an example of routine book production just before the advent of printing and contrasts with Dorchester's other important manuscript, the Wilton Psalter, on which hours of scribes' and illustrators' time was lavished. *The Canterbury Tales* was bound by Cockerell in the same style as the Psalter.

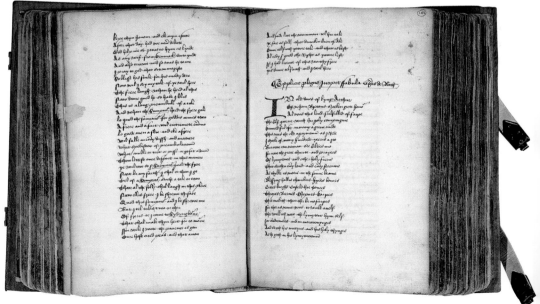

Plutarch. [Vitae]. *Venice: Nicolas Jenson, 1478.*

Jenson, a Frenchman, is thought to have been sent to Mainz in 1458 by the command of his king, Charles VII, to learn the new art of printing, with the intention of returning to set up a printing establishment in Paris. The death of the king put an end to the project and he established himself instead as a printer in Italy. His roman types are beautifully designed and proportioned and had a strong influence on type design.

Plutarch. [Vitae]. *Venice: Nicolas Jenson, 1478.*

Anon. L'art et instruction de bien dancer. *Paris: Michel Toulouze, c.1490.*

This short work on the art of *basse danse* is the earliest printed book on the subject of dancing. It is also one of the earliest examples, although not the first, of printed music. It is likely that the College possesses the only surviving copy of this work and no other copy has come to light since the first facsimile edition of it was published in 1936. The date of printing might be a little later than 1490, but the printer's address given in the colophon is one he left in 1496. Another facsimile edition published in 1971 included an English translation of the introductory text and a transcription of the music in modern notation.

Anon. L'art et instruction de bien dancer. *Paris: Michel Toulouze, c.1490. Colophon.*

Raoul Lefevre. The recuyell of the historyes of Troye. *Bruges: William Caxton and Colard Mansion, 1473.*

This is the first book to be printed in the English language. Caxton finished translating it from the French in Cologne in 1471 and to gain practical experience seems to have taken part in the printing of an edition of Bartholomaeus Anglicus' *De proprietatibus rerum*. He returned to England in 1476 and set up his printing press in premises in the precincts of Westminster Abbey, near to the seat of the court and Parliament, and remained there until his death in 1491.

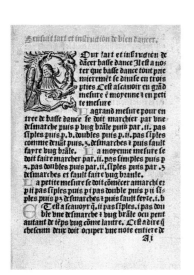

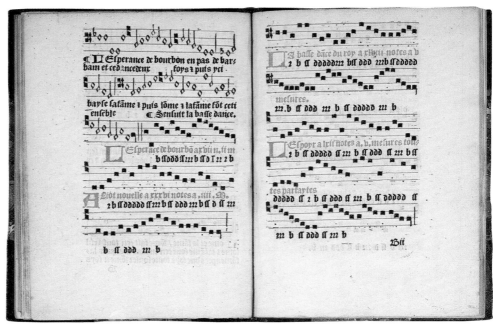

Anon. L'art et instruction de bien dancer. *Paris: Michel Toulouze, c.1490.*

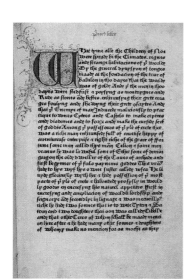

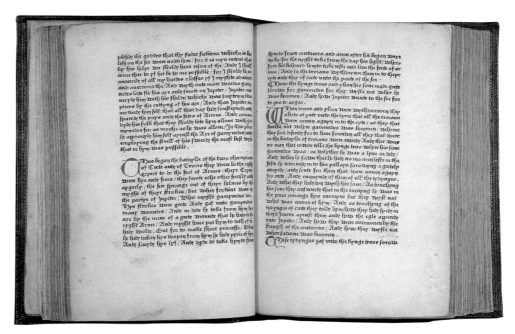

Raoul Lefevre. The recuyell of the historyes of Troye. *Bruges: William Caxton and Colard Mansion, 1473.*

Lloyd Roberts

David Lloyd Roberts (1835–1920), founder of the College's Lloyd Roberts lecture, was an obstetrician and gynaecologist. He was a well-known 'character' in Manchester where he practised, driving around town even in the twentieth century in a brougham, a carriage that had been designed in the late 1830s.

His definition of gynaecology was said to be 'anything either curable or lucrative'. A cultured man with wide interests, he collected furniture and art treasures as well as books. He bequeathed all his medical books to the College and the rest went to the John Rylands Library in Manchester. In terms of rarity this was probably the College's most notable acquisition since the Dorchester collection. Nearly half the College's incunabula came with the Lloyd Roberts bequest – originally it was thought that there were 53, but later research has revised some dates and 46 are now regarded as early enough to fit the definition. They include two copies of the 1478 *De medicina* of Celsus, one in an early binding (see illustration). Other notable rarities include the 1540 edition of Thomas Raynalde's *The byrth of mankynde*, possibly the first book printed in England to contain copperplate engravings.

Celsus, Aulus Cornelius. Medicinae libri viii. *Venice: Aldus, 1478.*

The Roman author of this work, written about AD 30, was not a medicus in the sense that he did not treat others for gain, but an estate owner who was likely to have used some of the therapies he describes to treat his family and his slaves. The printer, Aldus Manutius, was the leading publisher of his time. He was responsible for the introduction of the small book that could be held in one hand and would fit the pocket for which his type-designer, Francesco Griffo, created the italic font, narrower than the ordinary rounded roman type and based on the handwriting of the papal chancellery.

Osler

Sir William Osler, born at Bond Head, Ontario in 1849, was one of the greatest general physicians and medical educators, especially influential during his period as professor of medicine in the newly founded Johns Hopkins Hospital and Medical School from 1889 to 1905. He combined the English method of bedside teaching in small groups with the close co-operation of wards and laboratories that were a feature of the German medical schools.

At the College of which he became a Fellow in 1883, he was Harveian Orator and Goulstonian Lecturer but did not hold office, even when he was appointed regius professor of medicine in Oxford from 1905 till his death in 1919. He took a keen interest in the library and its treasures, especially when

David Lloyd Roberts (1835–1920). Oils on canvas by Sir William Orpen, 1923.

Below and bottom: *Celsus, Aulus Cornelius*. Medicinae libri viii. *Venice: Aldus, 1478.*

Sir William Osler (1849–1919). Oils on canvas, by Joyce Aris, 1960, after S. Seymour Thomas, 1908.

Auenbrugger's Inventum novum ex percussione thoracis humani ut signo abstrusos interni pectoris morbos detegendi *(Vienna, 1761).*

Davis Evan Bedford (1898–1978), 1961.

there was an exhibition to be organised. A noted bibliophile, his large collection of books and manuscripts (7,783 entries in the published catalogue) was bequeathed to his *alma mater*, McGill University, Montreal, except for a few of special interest he bequeathed to other libraries.

The College received two of these: a manuscript of Sir Theodore de Mayerne [see pages 48, 127] and the *Regulations and Transactions of the Glocestershire Medical Society* [see pages 88–90]. His donations to the College library during his life, though not numerous, were rare and valuable. They include a copy of the 1478 *De medicina* of Celsus (another given by David Lloyd Roberts is illustrated on page 77) and the Verona 1530 edition of Fracastoro's poem *Syphilis*. He also donated a copy of the first edition (1690) of John Locke's *An essay concerning humane understanding*, handsomely bound in blue morocco.

Auenbrugger's *Inventum novum ex percussione thoracis humani ut signo abstrusos interni pectoris morbos detegendi* (Vienna, 1761) was also part of the bequest; this is the book that introduced the idea of percussion of the chest as a diagnostic method. Osler bought this in Prague for 90 marks and, having acquired another copy in Rome for 1½ francs (*sic*), he gave it to the College. Inside the front cover, among other manuscript inscriptions, is Osler's note that he donated the book on 20 April 1909 (see illustration).

The Evan Bedford Cardiology Collection

Evan Bedford first began to comb the second-hand bookshops of London, Paris and Lyons for old works on the heart and its diseases when he was a Registrar in the 1920s, a habit which continued for many years, especially during his travels in wartime. As well as bookshops, booksellers' catalogues and auction sales became hunting grounds for this increasingly expert bibliophile and medical historian and eventually his collection resulted in his library of over 1,000 items. He turned his experiences into an article for the College *Journal*, published in 1972.

When he retired, Bedford began to think about a permanent home for his collection. He hoped to preserve it intact and received several tempting American bids. However, it was accepted by the College in early 1971 and, later that year, the Bedford collection became part of the Harveian Library. It was the single largest benefaction that the library received in the twentieth century and is housed as a separate collection in the gallery of the main Dorchester Library.

The value of this gift is further enhanced by the catalogue. Bedford edited and annotated his own working document with the help of Leonard Payne, formerly College librarian and Charles Newman, the then Harveian librarian. The structure reflects the way Bedford, as a clinician, viewed the history of cardiology.

The Evan Bedford Collection on the Dorchester Library gallery.

Anyone using the catalogue can easily find any item or any information they are seeking, thanks to the three separate indices – by name of author, subject and associations. This last refers to donors, bookplates, previous owners and the like. Thus, anyone who happens to wonder which books previously belonged to the Corfu Medical Book Society (only one in fact) will find it here. Another feature of the catalogue, which makes it a pleasure to read in its own right, is the profusion of annotations appended to many of the items. That Thomas Arnold, headmaster of Rugby, had only one coronary artery or that the first graphic representation of the arterial pulse was based on the movement of a leaf placed on the artery by the Pole Josephus Struthius in the sixteenth century are among the snippets.

There are 1,112 items in the collection, ranging in size from offprints of two or three pages to the 82 volumes of the *American Heart Journal*. Most of the collection consists of books written from several centuries BC to nearly the present day, and it is difficult to think of any important original text in the history of cardiology that is not there.

Bedford was careful to choose those editions of books that he considered most significant and, unlike most book-collectors, he saw no particular merit in first editions. Thus, it was the second edition of Peacock's book on malformations of the human heart, the standard work on congenital heart disease for many years, which he preferred to the shorter first edition. Likewise, the third edition of 1839 of Hope's textbook is the one in the collection; this Bedford described as a 'masterpiece' and 'mandatory reading for a cardiologist even today' – a remark which is a victory for optimism over realism, one fears.

Some important publications were in the form of articles in journals and Bedford sometimes had to purchase a run of several volumes of a journal to obtain the one containing the article he was seeking.

In many libraries books and journals would be held separately but Bedford kept articles among the related textbooks. So, for example, between and within a few inches of shelf of Burns's and Hope's books, are Volume 4 of *Dublin Hospital Reports* containing Robert Adams's first description of Adams-Stokes syndrome and Volume 37 of the *Edinburgh Medical Journal* with Dominic Corrigan's account of aortic regurgitation.

In addition to the primary sources, there is a considerable amount of secondary material, mostly biographical, in the collection. Biographies and other publications dealing with individual authors stand next to that author's own publications. Collective biographies are kept with an impressive number of books on the history of medicine in general or of cardiology in particular. All these are well annotated in the catalogue similarly to the primary material.

Reading all his supplementary comments one can only conclude that Bedford had read nearly everything in the collection attentively and perceptively – a remarkable achievement for a busy practising clinician.

Other Important Books

*Saint Augustine of Hippo. [*The City of God */ with the commentaries of Thomas Waley and Nicholas Trivet]. Mainz: Peter Schoeffer, 1473.*

The earliest printed books did not have title pages, but the first page usually started *Incipit* (meaning 'Here beginneth ...'), followed by the title or subject of the work and sometimes the name of the author. The colophon at the end of the book gave the information about where, when and by whom the book was printed. The printers were continuing the conventions of manuscript books. The colophon in this book adds an assurance that it was produced not with a pen, but with the 'heads of type-letters'. Schoeffer, a former servant of the inventor of movable type, Johann Gutenberg, may have thought this necessary because of the story of the arrest in Paris of his partner, Johann Fust, on a charge of sorcery. Although experienced scribes were able to produce letters that resembled each other closely, it seems that some readers

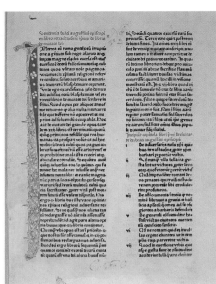

were startled to find the letters looking exactly alike at each appearance in the text. This book was one of four incunabula bequeathed by Professor Roy Dobbin FRCP and has inside the front cover the bookplate of a previous owner Count Suchtelen (1751–1836) and a book label from the Imperial Library of St Petersburg.

Saint Augustine of Hippo. [The City of God / with the commentaries of Thomas Waley and Nicholas Trivet]. Mainz: Peter Schoeffer, 1473.

Saint Thomas Aquinas. De occultorum nature effectuum, proprii cordis motus causas declarantes studentibus physice summe necessarii. *Leipzig: Jacobus Thanner, 1499.*

This pamphlet contains two parts: *De occultis nature operibus* and *De motu cordis*. Printed over 20 years after Augustine's *City of God*, this book has a title page, on which the author's name and standing serve to give authority to the text. This suggests an appreciation that a formal opening to a work would help advertise it. Aquinas saw in man, as it were, a world in miniature and argued that the heart in an animal was like that of the heavens in the universe: 'it had a motion, not circular but like a circular motion, made up of forces of traction and propulsion.' The doctrine of the microcosmic cycle, of which this treatise is an important source, became widely known and may have been familiar to Harvey. This rare tract was purchased at the sale of books belonging to former Harveian librarian, Archibald Gilpin.

Saint Thomas Aquinas. De occultorum nature effectuum ... *Leipzig: Jacobus Thanner, 1499 (the second part, De motu cordis).*

Andreas Vesalius. De humani corporis fabrica. *Basel: Joannes Oporinus, 1543.*

Towards the end of the Middle Ages the Church gradually relaxed its prohibitions on the dissection of human bodies. When the Black Death emerged in 1348 the papacy approved post-mortem examination in the attempt to discover the cause of plague, but it was not until 1537 that anatomy teaching

81

Andreas Vesalius. De humani corporis fabrica. *Basel: Joannes Oporinus, 1543.*

by dissection was officially approved. Vesalius, who was originally from Brussels, taught anatomy at the University of Padua, where William Harvey was later to study. His work 'On the fabric of the human body' established observed fact and demonstration as the basis of anatomical study rather than appeal to traditional authority. This brought him into conflict at several points with the teachings of Galen (AD 129–*c*.216) whose writings on anatomy had virtually been law for more than 1,300 years. Ironically, Vesalius was following Galen's advice to see for himself. For example, he made it clear that he could not see the interventricular pores that Galen had claimed allowed blood to pass from one side of the heart to the other. This led eventually to the need for a different explanation of the heart's activity and the way the blood moved around the body. The drawings, probably by Jan Stephan van Calcar, are still unsurpassed as illustrations of gross anatomy.

George Edwards. A natural history of uncommon birds. *London: for the Author, 1743–51.*

George Edwards (1694–1773) was born in Stratford, then part of rural Essex. When apprenticed to a London merchant he discovered he hated trade and left in 1716. He lived in what he described as self-confessed idleness but studied natural history and learned to draw or paint what he saw. He made two long journeys abroad, to Scandinavia and France, coming home in 1721 to resume his studies. His pictures came to the attention of Fellows of the Royal Society who began to employ him to record their collections of rare birds. To his surprise they paid him for his work.

Some examples of the work of George Edwards, all of which are held by the College library.

Main picture: *Peacock pheasant (plate 67), from* A natural history of uncommon birds, *vol. 2.*
Below left: *Red-belly'd bluebird and Scarlet locust (plate 22), from* A natural history of uncommon birds, *vol. 1.*
Below: *the title spread of* A natural history of uncommon birds.

His chief patron was Sir Hans Sloane, President of both the College and the Royal Society and a great collector, who made the College appoint him as Bedell. As such he was administrator and keeper of the library and his ample apartments in the College provided him with a studio to carry on his work as a recording artist. Dealing mainly with dead specimens of rare birds from abroad, he concentrated on an accurate and natural portrayal.

Anxious to publish the contents of his portfolio he learnt to etch, taught by Mark Catesby, artist and natural historian. Using the College as a publishing house Edwards produced his first volume *A natural history of uncommon birds* in 1743, with his own text and hand-coloured etchings. This was an instant success, gaining him a nomination for Fellowship of the Royal Society, an honour that he refused. Three volumes followed, published in 1747, 1750 and 1751. Each was accompanied by a French edition.

Edwards announced that age and infirmity precluded further work, but by then he was a famous ornithologist, awarded the Copley Medal of the Royal Society in 1750 and, after Sloane's retirement, better known in the world of science than any of the College Presidents he served. Edwards did not, however, stop working. In 1754 he published a new edition of Catesby's book on the natural history of Carolina. He continued his own work with a new title, *Gleanings of natural history*, published in 1757 and 1760.

With the publication of the second volume he resigned as Bedell, sold his portfolio to Lord Bute and, again, announced that he had finished working. Retiring to Plaistow, he continued to visit the College and the Royal Society. Once again, he did not stop work, publishing a third volume of *Gleanings* in 1764, mainly depicting South American birds captured from a French ship by Captain Washington Shirley, later Lord Ferrers. The College library holds all Edwards's volumes, hand-coloured by himself, that can be seen and admired.

Fore-edge Paintings

Fore-edge painting is an English invention of the Commonwealth period – mid-seventeenth century – described by bookbinder Bernard Middleton as the first completely frivolous binding practice. Partially concealed during routine handling, the painting is viewed by gently splaying the horizontally held fore-edge leaves of the book. During painting, the edges of the leaves are scraped, the paper sized, the paint neither wet nor dry and the colours over-bright to balance the gilding with which these fine bindings are often decorated.

Most fore-edge paintings are on the upper side enabling the artist to brush down the slightly overlapping pages. A cartoon of the definitive version is often seen on the lower edge but entirely different double fore-edge paintings are also occasionally seen.

The practice is linked generally to the early eighteenth-century bookbinder John Brindley. These images were typically floral or heraldic but the Halifax firm of William Edwards (1723–1808) specialised in fore-edge paintings of country houses, rural abbeys and landscapes; these are often signed 'Edwards f[e]c[i]t'.

The book trade seemed to lose interest in fore-edge painting during the 1830s but there has been a twentieth-century resurgence with an active forgery market reproducing images on books in original eighteenth-century bindings.

Three books held in the College library have fore-edge paintings:

1. *Edward Young*. Night thoughts and a paraphrase on part of the book of Job. *London: Chiswick Press, 1812.*

A late edition in original red-grained morocco binding with gold-tooled surround and eight raised gold-decorated bands on the spine. It is inscribed in pencil 'Scene from the Poem "Night Thoughts"; "With swelling sails made good the promised port" page 212'. The painting is a seascape depicting a view towards the shore showing two Mediterranean towns separated by an inlet with mountains in the background, a pair of two-masted barques – the nearer in full sail – four other sailing boats and a rowing skiff in the foreground. It has loosely inserted a manuscript presentation letter dated 'Jan 30/34' addressed 'Dear Chaplin' and signed 'Robt Hutchison'. [Thomas Hancock] Arnold Chaplin (1864–1944: Harveian librarian 1918–44) and [Sir] Robert Hutchison (1871–1960: PRCP 1938–41) may have discussed this donation at one of the College Club dinners which both regularly attended during the 1930s.

Edward Young. Night thoughts and a paraphrase on part of the book of Job. *London: Chiswick Press, 1812. Also showing the technique for viewing fore-edge paintings. The painting is of a seascape depicting a view towards the shore showing two Mediterranean towns.*

Samuel Johnson. Sermons *left for publication by John Taylor, printed by J. Procter at Ripon (Yorkshire), 1835. Painting on fore-edge: 'Dr Johnson's House, Lichfield'.*

2. Samuel Johnson. Sermons *left for publication by John Taylor, printed by J. Procter at Ripon (Yorkshire), 1835. Provenance unknown.*

In original dark-red grained morocco boards with blind tooling and five gold panels with blind decorated inserts on the spine. A small label inside the front cover reads 'Bound by Procter & Vickers, Ripon'. It is inscribed 'Painting on fore-edge. Dr Johnson's House, Lichfield'. The painting depicts a townscape with three houses in profile and a hansom cab in front, a street with traders and awnings in perspective to the right, two central monuments and several figures.

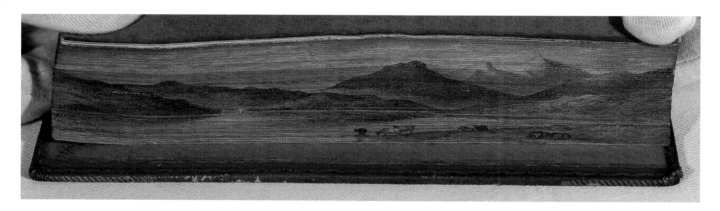

Sir Walter Scott. The Lord of the Isles: a poem. *Edinburgh: Constable, 1815. The fore-edge painting depicts a seascape at the Isle of Arran.*

3. Sir Walter Scott. The Lord of the Isles: a poem. *Edinburgh: Constable, 1815. Provenance unknown.*

In original red-grained morocco with gold-tooled and blind stamped decorations on the boards, and four raised bands with decorated gold-tooled devices on the spine. The fore-edge painting is a seascape at the Isle of Arran. It depicts a mountain landscape viewed from the sea or a loch with eight cattle posed in the foreground on a spit of land separated from the mainland by water.

Manuscript Collections

The College has accumulated a varied collection of manuscripts, mainly as gifts. In a catalogue of 1727 there were 83 entries for manuscripts; in 1827 there were 198 and the 1928 catalogue has over 400, which by then included some College archives. Manuscripts are not easy to quantify because they may comprise single sheets or volumes, folders holding a few sheets, or groups containing hundreds of items, but there are now around 500 collections of which about half contain only one item.

Receipt books (household remedies and recipes) from the sixteenth century onwards, diaries and prescription books form significant and expected groups, and give a fascinating record of changing views of medicine, astronomy and astrology. There are several thousand signed letters written by or to doctors. The letters of Baldwin Hamey (1600–76) and his notebook *Bustorum aliquot reliquae* are useful sources of information about his contemporaries. Some valuable non-medical manuscripts also find a place, notably the mid-thirteenth century illuminated Wilton Psalter and a late fifteenth-century manuscript of Chaucer's *The Canterbury Tales* which came with the library bequeathed by the Marquis of Dorchester in the seventeenth century [see pages 73–6].

The papers of some past Presidents of the College have been acquired through their descendants – for example a substantial archive of the personal and professional papers of Lord Brain (PRCP 1950–7), and a smaller collection from Sir Charles Dodds (PRCP 1962–6). Papers of the longest-serving President, Sir Henry Halford (PRCP 1820–44) are on indefinite loan to the College.

Manuscript sources for famous patients include Thomas Marwood's casebook with an account of the last illness and post-mortem of King James I and physicians' bulletins on the state of health of George III. There are also journals written by Sir James Clark containing notes of his journeys with the royal family between 1847 and 1868 and the papers of Sir Edward Henry Sieveking including his diaries as physician to the Prince of Wales between 1864 and 1873. Sir William Henry Broadbent's narrative of the last illness and death of Prince Albert Edward ('Eddy'), Duke of Clarence (1892), is there as well.

The College collections also contain papers relating to the last illness of Benjamin Disraeli (1881), the medical history of Anthony Eden, and two reports on Sir Winston Churchill's medical problems, as well as the last illness of his father, Lord Randolph Churchill (1895). (Patient notes are closed for 100 years after death.)

A few collections of papers from institutions and societies are also held by the College: the Association of Physicians of Great Britain and Ireland, for example, and three London dispensaries – Drury Lane (1782–1952), Western (Marylebone) (1833–1949) and the Westminster General (1774–1949).

The 66 oriental manuscripts, mostly in Arabic or Persian, dating from the twelfth to twentieth centuries, have been received as gifts or bequests made from the seventeenth to the twentieth centuries [see page 88].

Avicenna's Canon of medicine, *1214.*

An illustration from the seventeenth-to-eighteenth-century illustrated manuscript of Mansur's Anatomy.

Oriental Manuscripts

There are nearly 70 items in the College's collection of oriental manuscripts, mostly in Arabic or Persian. The first acquisitions were the bequest of John Selden, constitutional lawyer, MP for Oxford University in the Long Parliament and noted Arabist. Most of his Arabic manuscripts went to the Bodleian Library in Oxford but 11 of medical interest came to the College on his death in 1654. They include the oldest volume in the College library, the copy of Avicenna's *Canon of medicine* dated 1214 (611 in the Islamic calendar).

Roy Dobbin FRCP (1873–1939), while professor of obstetrics and gynae-cology in Cairo, was keen to fill gaps in the College's small collection of Arabic work and eventually donated 31 Arabic and Persian manuscripts. They include the commentary on the anatomy of Avicenna by Ibn al-Nafis (d.1288), which includes the earliest known description of the pulmonary circulation.

The remaining Persian manuscripts came from Cyril Lloyd Elgood FRCP (1892–1970), the author of *A medical history of Persia and the eastern caliphate* and *Safavid medical practice* and *Safavid surgery*. They include a seventeenth-to-eighteenth-century illustrated manuscript of Mansur's *Anatomy*. The collection was catalogued by Professor A. S. Tritton in 1951 for the *Journal of the Royal Asiatic Society.*

Wilton Psalter. c.1250, written probably at Salisbury for use at Wilton Abbey (MS).

The reference in the book to Saint Edith, a former abbess, indicates that this richly ornamented Psalter, written on vellum, was meant for use at Wilton Abbey in Wiltshire. Two illustrations that each take up about half a page remain in the volume: the Holy Spirit descending appears in the initial D of *Dominus illuminatio mea* (Psalm 27 in the English Authorised version) on folio 33 recto; and a picture of King David arguing with a fool in the initial D of *Dixit insipiens in corde suo* (Psalm 53) on folio 66 verso.

There are also many smaller illustrations throughout the volume – in the calendar that precedes the psalms and in the initial capital letters which begin the psalms. The volume was rebound by the Cockerell bindery in 1951 with oak boards and silver clasps.

Folio 8 recto is also illustrated with an eagle taking a lamb in the initial C of *Cum invocarem* (Psalm 4); and both folios 156 verso and 157 recto, that include a goat playing a viol in the D of *Defecit insalutare tuum anima* (Psalm 119, verse 81).

Regulations and Transactions of the Glocestershire Medical Society Instituted May 1788.

The surviving papers of the Glocestershire (*sic*) Medical Society, dating from 30 July 1788 to 5 June 1793, are bound in one foolscap-size volume, consisting of title page, regulations, minutes, and several short papers. It is one of two manuscripts that Sir William Osler bequeathed to the Royal

The Wilton Psalter, c.1250, written probably at Salisbury for use at Wilton Abbey (MS).

Clockwise from above left: the Holy Spirit descending; King David arguing with a fool; the binding of oak boards and silver clasps; an eagle taking a lamb; a goat playing a viol.

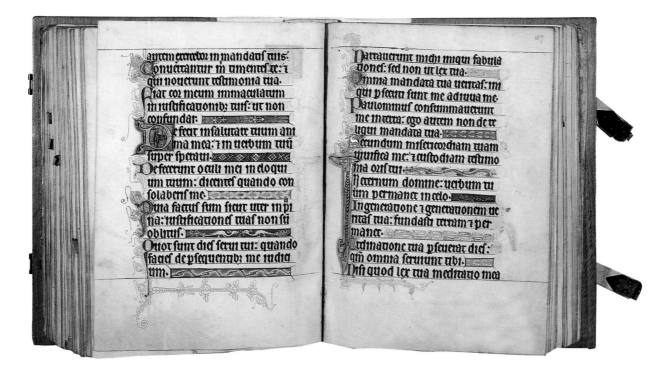

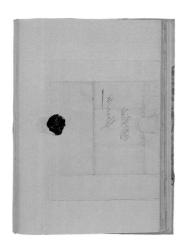

Letter addressed to John Heathfield Hickes from Mr Matthews of Fairford.

Dr Hickes's paper on the eruptive fever of 1789 in Gloucestershire.

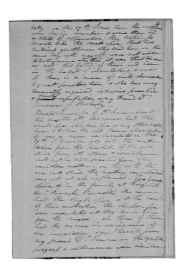

College of Physicians. Its existence had been known since extracts were published with comments in the *British Medical Journal* in 1896, before Osler acquired it.

The five members of the Society, dubbed the Medico-Convivial Society by Edward Jenner – Caleb Hillier Parry, John Heathfield Hickes, Thomas Paytherus, Daniel Ludlow and Jenner, all Gloucestershire medical practitioners – met in the Fleece Inn, Rodborough. The volume includes two fragments in Jenner's hand. One is on mitral stenosis (30 July 1788) and the second, a brief undated note on an eruptive disease usually called by the people of Gloucestershire the swine or pig-pox, but sometimes the cowpox. Members of the society believed that the infection was 'capable of preserving the Patient from the infection of the small-Pox'. He mentions that the society's members have been 'engaged in an experiment' inquiry into the nature of this disease'.

The most significant paper for the history of vaccination, and the longest in the volume, is the 14-page 'Observations & Experiments made upon persons labouring under an eruptive fever which appeared in several parts of Glos'tershire in the latter end of 1789' by John Heathfield Hickes (1751–1808). The minutes show that Hickes originally read a paper on this subject on 28 July 1790 and that he and Jenner communicated 'some further particulars relative to the Swine Pox' in September 1790. But the version preserved must have been rewritten in the second half of 1792.

In addition to his own observations made at the Gloucester Infirmary and elsewhere in Gloucestershire, Hickes also encouraged surgeons in other parts of the county to try inoculating patients with smallpox. He suggested treating patients who had had the so-called swine pox, but no other eruptive fever as far as could be ascertained, and to observe the reaction. The paper is followed by five letters from three of the local medical practitioners describing their clinical experiences. Hickes thought the pustules of swine-pox were of a different colour and shape from those of smallpox, but his correspondents were generally unable to distinguish between the two. Jenner is mentioned as inoculating his son Edward with the 'swine pox' and subsequently with smallpox. In his 1798 *An inquiry into the causes and effects of the variolae vaccinae* Jenner said of this outbreak, 'I consider it then as a variety of the Small-pox.'

Personal Collections

Richard Bright

Richard Bright (1789–1858) was the son of a Bristol merchant and banker who attended a school in Bristol run by a local Unitarian minister. His medical education in Edinburgh was interrupted by a visit to Iceland and a period in London studying in the medical school of Guy's and St Thomas's Hospitals, and he graduated MD at Edinburgh in 1812.

He journeyed through Austria to Hungary in 1814 and observed the medical practice in the hospitals of Berlin and Vienna. He was admitted as a Licentiate of the College in 1816 and a Fellow in 1832. In 1820 he became assistant physician to Guy's Hospital and full physician in 1824.

Bright is best known for his description of dropsy – oedema associated with kidney disease – in which the urine can be coagulated by heat owing to the presence of albumin, subsequently known as 'Bright's disease'. The observation of albumin in the urine had been observed before, but it was Bright who made the connection with diseased kidney (glomuleronephritis) and made the synthesis of the three linked symptoms. This disease is described in the first volume of his illustrated *Reports on medical cases* (1827) in which the clinical picture during life is correlated with the pathology of the internal organs of several parts of the body. A second part published in 1831 is entirely concerned with the nervous system, with the illustrations in a separate volume.

Although his name is generally thought of in relation to diseases of the viscera, especially the kidney, Bright also made numerous observations of neurological conditions, both in the work just mentioned and in papers that he contributed to the *Guy's Hospital Reports*.

Richard Bright (1789–1858). Oils on canvas by Frederick Richard Say, 1860.

Main picture: *Kidney in dropsy*, Reports on medical cases, *vol.1, plate 1.*

Below: *watercolours of the liver in dropsy, MS.974/86a.*

Bottom: *Liver in dropsy*, Reports ..., *vol.1, plate 6.*

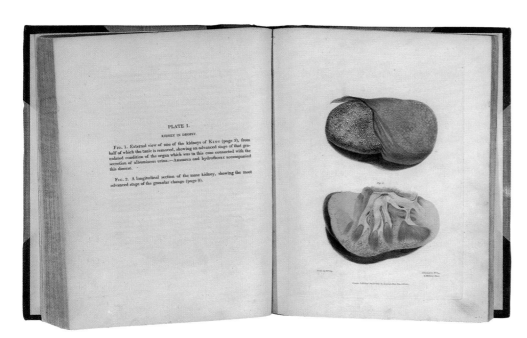

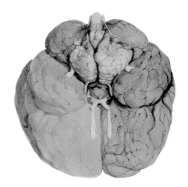

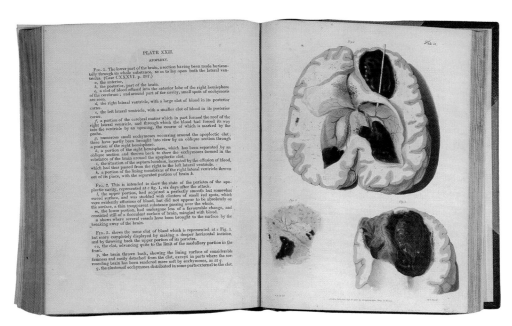

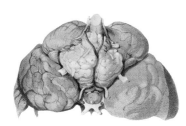

Main picture: *Apoplexy,*
Reports on medical cases
vol.2, plate 22.

Top: *watercolour of a Tumour
of the Pons varioli,
MS.974/22a.*

Above: *Tumour of the Pons
varioli,* Reports ... *vol.2, plate
2, fig.2.*

Francis Sibson.
Facing page, top to bottom:
*A diagram and its black-and-
white equivalent in the printed paper, 1844.
Colour lithograph of an
1869 watercolour in* Medical
anatomy.

The Bright pictorial archive consists of watercolours and some pencil drawings of cases under his care, mainly colour illustrations of diseased organs, all mounted on card. A substantial number are by F. R. Say who later painted Bright's portrait. There are 98 boards in the collection and several have two or more drawings on them, totalling over 300 illustrations. A few were clearly reproduced in the Reports on medical cases, but not all the illustrations in the published volumes are represented by originals or prototypes in the College collection and there are many drawings in the collection which have not been printed anywhere.

Francis Sibson FRCP FRS (1814–76)

Born in Cumbria, but brought up in Edinburgh from the age of five, Francis Sibson's earliest medical experience was as an apprentice to Edinburgh surgeon and anatomist, John Lizars (1794–1860). In 1833 he spent some time in the pathology department at Guy's Hospital, London, where he earned the admiration of the curator, Dr Thomas Hodgkin (1798–1866). He was appointed surgeon to the Nottingham General Hospital in 1835 and remained there until he was elected one of three physicians to the newly established St Mary's Hospital, London, in 1851.

The Sibson pictorial archive consists of 382 watercolours and drawings given to the College library in 1877 by his widow. They resulted from his work in trying to envisage the viscera in health and disease. In his paper 'On changes induced in the situation and structure of the internal organs ... and on the nature and external indications of these changes' published in the *Transactions of the Provincial Medical and Surgical Association* in 1844, he demonstrated his method of creating diagrams. These showed the sizes and positions of the internal organs at post-mortem and ascertaining comparative views in life, using the recently developed diagnostic aids of percussion and auscultation. Hodgkin wrote that, 'It is calculated to be a vast assistance to clinical medicine.'

As well as sketches for the 1844 paper, the archive includes many water-colours of the type lithographed for his book *Medical anatomy ...* (1869). These give much more detailed views of the internal organs, though based on similar methods. The idea of 'medical anatomy', Sibson explained, was 'to teach the topographical anatomy of the healthy viscera on the dead body. Afterwards [the teacher of pathology] might indicate to [the pupils] on the living body, the varying position of the organs during the healthy exercise of their functions ... the student ought to be as familiar with the position and movements of the organs as if he saw them stripped of their parietes and exposed to view.'

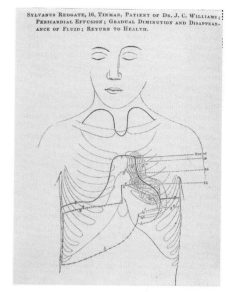

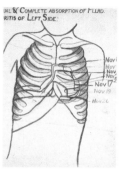

The Pictorial Collections of Willan and Bateman

Robert Willan (1757–1812) and his pupil Thomas Bateman (1778–1821) were the founders of modern dermatology. Willan was the first person to 'arrange diseases of the skin in a clear and intelligible manner' which he did by classi-fying each disease in one of eight 'orders': papulae, squamae, exanthemata, bullae, pustulae, vesiculae, tubercula, maculae.

The library holds an important collection of Willan's and Bateman's manuscripts and publications, including approximately 160 watercolour drawings made between 1792 and 1814. Some of the drawings were made by Bateman and are either signed 'TB' or include the words 'Drawn by TB'. The remaining drawings were produced by other artists and although many of them are unsigned, slight differences in style are evident. Comments or instructions for the engraver or printer are written on some of the drawings, e.g. 'to be more softened down' and 'not so dark'. The illustration of acne indurata includes the comment: 'The inflammation faded and must be height-ened' which has also been initialled 'TB'.

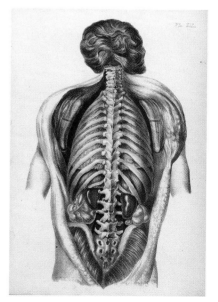

The watercolours were drawn for Willan's *Description and treatment of cutaneous diseases* which he started to publish as a series in 1798. Following his death the drawings were acquired by Bateman. He completed Willan's series and then used some of the drawings in his own *Delineations of cutaneous diseases* (1817). However, many of them remain unpublished.

The College also has the manuscript of Bateman's *Delineations* (purchased from Sotheby's in 1906) in which the text is exactly as printed in 1817, apart from two short additional notes. This publication was particularly important because it contains descriptions of herpes iris (now known as erythema multiforme) and eczema due to external irritation. It also contains the first description of molluscum contagiosum with Bateman's own drawing. The manuscript of the *Delineations* includes 72 illustrations. The first six are engravings taken from Willan's *On cutaneous diseases* (1808), the others are original watercolours, some of which were redrawn from earlier versions.

93

Brown-Séquard Collection

Dr Charles Édouard Brown-Séquard, born in Mauritius in 1817, citizen of Britain, France and America, is well known for his spinal cord syndrome, but remains unrecognised as a pioneer of endocrinology, experimentally demonstrating the significance of the adrenal glands.

A small, very likeable man, he engaged in ferocious animal experiments, a practice acceptable in his day. He came to London in 1859, became a founder physician of the National Hospital for Nervous Diseases, and was elected to Fellowships of the Royal College of Physicians and the Royal Society. After four years in London, he decided to give all his time to experimental work in France, succeeding Claude Bernard as Professor of Physiology at the College de France. He continued to produce major scientific works until his death in

The Dorchester Library today.

Paris in 1894. There is still little recognition of the immense contribution he made to modern medical thinking.

At the 1960 Centenary celebrations of the National Hospital, W. G. discovered, by a most curious coincidence, that the daughter of Brown-Séquard had married and Irish surgeon named McCausland: and that the name McCausland appeared twice in the list of former pupils of Winchester College. Dr Charles Edward McCausland was a general practitioner in Folkestone and his son an army officer. These two men proved to be the grandson and great-grandson of Brown-Séquard. Dr McCausland had a collection of papers, letters and personal items belonging to his grandfather which form the Gooddy/McCausland collection in the College library, having been delivered there by Colonel Ian McCausland in 1967.

This collection provides a great amount of historical and social detail, provided mainly in letters from some of the most important British, French and American figures of the second half of the nineteenth century, including Charles Darwin, T. H. Huxley, and James Paget (invitation to meet the future King Edward VII). Darwin wrote requesting a favourable review for the French edition of *The origin of species*. Louis Pasteur addresses Brown-Séquard as 'Cher grand Maître'. Larrey, Eiffel, Vulpian, Charcot, Renan, de Lesseps, Broca, Prince Bonaparte, Louis Agassiz, and Oliver Wendell Holmes are among many other eminent names.

A beautiful pink watered-silk sash of the Brazilian Order of the Rose, presented for personal services by Dom Pedro II, Emperor of Brazil, forms part of the collection.

5

The Archives

The College has an almost complete record of its proceedings from its foundation in 1518, although only a limited amount of material is preserved from the period before 1666 owing to the destruction of the College building in the Great Fire of London.

Its archives comprise approximately 2,000 items making up around 130 metres of catalogued documents. They are consulted not only by Fellows and Members, College officers and staff, but also by historians, the media and genealogists. Although some categories within the archives had been transferred to the care of the library earlier, it is only within the last 20 years that all but the most recent documents have been made the responsibility of the library staff.

By agreement with the Registrar, who is responsible for current records, the *Annals* are now available for consultation by the public after 10 years, and other College records after 20 years unless they are deemed to be confidential.

The proceedings of Comitia (meetings of the Fellows), known as the *Annals*, form the core of the College record [see pages 98–9]. For a more detailed picture of the College's business and professional interests the *Annals* are supplemented by minutes and papers from other standing committees: Finance (accounts and financial papers from 1664), Council, Library, Museum and Building Committees. The minutes of the Censors' Board, included in the *Annals* until 1938, record the examining and disciplinary activities as required by the Charter 'to discourage the unskilfulness and temerity of … knavish men' and also matters of internal discipline and professional etiquette. Other committee papers document specific problems and projects – medical reform and examinations; the *Nomenclature of diseases*; the influenza epidemic of 1782–3, vaccination (1806–7 and 1871) and leprosy (1858–98); right up to the minutes of the many standing committees and working parties of recent times.

Legal documents such as royal charters [see pages 99–102] and trust deeds endowing College lectures, scholarships and research grants, and land rights for College property form another important group of documents. The

College also holds plans and illustrations of its premises, past and present. Those of St Andrews Place are consulted not only for building maintenance purposes, but are also of great interest to students of architecture.

Lists of Fellows and Licentiates (1673–date), Members (1859–date) and College officers are kept either in printed, typescript or manuscript form.

Texts (printed or manuscript) have been preserved of many of the lectures given at the College from 1661 onwards, though these are now more often kept as audio tapes. In the late 1960s an oral history programme was begun with audio-taped interviews by the Harveian librarian of notable older Fellows, the intention being to supplement the record of 'Munk's Roll' [see pages 55–6]. This changed in the mid-1980s to a videotape programme run in conjunction with Oxford Brookes University, which was subsequently expanded by the University to include many medical scientists who are not Fellows of the College.

The College Arms

The College received its Grant of Arms in 1546. The Grant is a colourful document although the arms are poorly depicted. The original description makes it clear that the hand from out of a cloud is 'ffelinge the powllse of an arm' and that the blob of fruit is a 'powme granate golde'. The choice of a pomegranate may have been from its alleged power to cure 'burning agues'.

A blazon of arms set on a shield was a design favoured by the Colleges of Oxford and Cambridge, whereas City Livery Companies preferred at least a crest above the shield and supporters to the side. The physicians were obviously keen to show their academic status as distinct from the Livery Companies of craft and trade.

When Dr Caius designed the College seal he did not copy the arms, using a picture of St Luke reading instead; however the 'hand on wrist' was put at the bottom. A good copy of the original arms was inscribed on the silver top of the porter's staff in 1679.

In the nineteenth century there were many variations in design without compromising the pattern of the original blazon. The 1546 design was faith-fully copied but much better drawn by Reynolds Stone to decorate the fourth volume of Munk's Roll. In 1963 the Treasurer, R. R. Bomford, commissioned the College of Arms to make a new design indicating the correct method of feeling a pulse. As a teacher he used the original design as an illustration of how not to do it. However, the College has so far adhered to the traditional representations of the arms and has not made use of the Bomford design.

Above: *The Grant of Arms, 1546.*

Above middle: *the arms in the College entrance hall.*

Above right: *the arms commissioned by R. R. Bomford, showing the correct method of feeling a pulse.*

Annals

Dr John Caius, when first elected President in 1555, decided that the College should have more formal procedures and that it should make a formal record of its meetings. He filled in the gaps for the period from 1518 as best he could from notes he found and memories he could draw on, but the result is inevitably patchy.

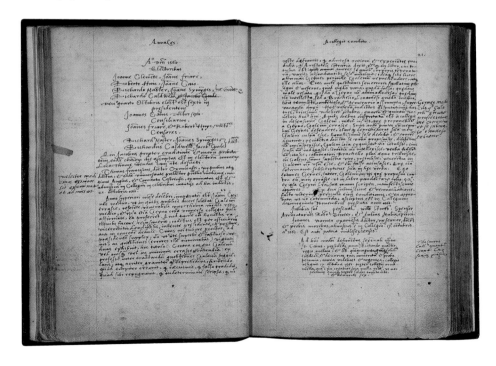

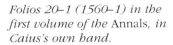

Folios 20–1 (1560–1) in the first volume of the Annals, *in Caius's own hand.*

98

His own record covers the nine years of his presidency (1555–61; 1562–4; and 1571–2) and the first volume of *Annals* is in his own hand. None of his contemporaries and successors kept minutes but it was for this purpose that the office of Registrar was created in 1579.

In the first five volumes the minutes were written almost entirely in Latin, although letters written to the College in English were transcribed into the *Annals*, not translated, as were the College's replies. The proceedings of the Building Committee for the College's premises in Warwick Lane were also recorded in English. The odd mixture of Latin and English in 1688–90 suggests that the Fellows (or the Registrar) could not decide whether to change or not. Volume 5 tailed off in January 1691 and from October of that year, when volume 6 began, the record has been in English. The only other gap until the present is 1771–81 for which volume 14 is missing.

The early volumes were given a Latin title beginning *Liber annalium* and the first volumes in English were known as *The Register Book* (kept by the 'Register' as he was called at the time). *Annals* is now generally accepted as both a briefer name and a uniform title for the whole series.

The *Annals* contain the minutes of Comitia: elections, prosecutions of unlicensed practitioners of medicine when this was part of the College's work, and its official relations with outside bodies. Events other than the College's formal meetings have not always been recorded consistently.

It might be possible, for example in the sixteenth and seventeenth centuries, to find a note of a lecturer's appointment by Comitia, but rarely any confirmation of the date on which the lectures were actually delivered. Censors' Board, or Comitia minora minutes were also included until they became a separate series in 1938. The nineteenth-century creations, the Council and the Finance Committee, have had their own series from the outset.

Annals, vol.5, folio 108 verso (December 1689). Latin is mixed with English, even in the same paragraph, as the College hesitated over the language to be used.

Charters

Foundation Charter

The Foundation Charter of September 1518 was ratified by Parliament on 15 April 1523, the only College charter that received this legal confirmation. It was not superseded by any of the unconfirmed Stuart charters. The four Censors it specified still exist as members of the Education, Training and Examinations Board. Its other provisions were abolished by subsequent Acts of Parliament and it can now be taken to express only the monarch's general approbation.

The document ought to have looked more attractive, but the large, elaborate H beginning the king's name (Henricus) and the other capital letters for which spaces were left on the top line were never inserted [see illustration on page 102].

James I Charter

In December 1616 a committee was appointed to consult lawyers about drawing up a petition for a new charter. Recent court cases, particularly that against Dr Bonham [see page 29] had left the College feeling that its position needed to be strengthened. It was deemed especially desirable that the College should have the power to summon all practitioners, to administer oaths to witnesses and to take bonds of those who were fined. The Charter, dated 8 October 1617 (presumed lost in the 1666 fire), made little difference in practice. And no bill was presented to the next Parliament in 1621–2 to confirm it. So this became the first of the Stuart charters that failed to gain any legal force.

Cromwell Charter

[OLIVER, Lord Protector. Exemplification. Letters patent (Inspeximus) exemplifying the Charter of Incorporation of 10 Henry VIII ... 8 November 1656. Endorsed on outside as folded: An Exemplification at the Request of Edward Alstone doctor in Physicke.]

Political changes in England in the early 1640s were reflected in the College's governing body by the election of men sympathetic with the aims of the Parliamentary party. Othowell Meverall, the new President elected in October 1641, was a graduate of the Puritan-influenced Christ's College, Cambridge. Among those who became elects at the same time was John Clarke, also of Christ's College, Meverall's successor who, as President from 1645 to 1650, helped to organise medical aid for the Parliamentary Army.

Because the government countenanced a variety of approaches to medicine, the College found it difficult to prosecute unlicensed practitioners during much of the Interregnum period. However, the establishment of the Protectorate under Oliver Cromwell at the end of 1653 seemed to present an opportunity for the College to reaffirm its authority. The influence in College affairs around that time of Fellows sympathetic to the government is demonstrated by their continued exclusion from the Fellowship of the former royal physician Walter Charleton. This contrasts with their determination to elect William Petty, who was influential with the government, despite his lack of response to several summonses to Comitia during his absence in Ireland.

In November 1656 the College obtained a charter from the Lord Protector confirming the provisions of its original charter from Henry VIII. But when the College brought an empiric to court later in November the case was thrown out on a dubious technicality – supposedly the original 1523 Act had not been registered with the king's signature. A second charter confirming the 1523 Act of Parliament, obtained in December 1657 was no greater help and this phase of the College's efforts to re-establish its authority over unapproved practitioners came to an end. All this took place under the leadership of the Suffolk puritan Edward Alston, elected President in October 1656, who remained in office until 1667 and presided over the campaign to obtain a new charter from King Charles II.

John Clarke (1582?–1653).
Oils on canvas, artist and
date unknown.

Charles II Charter

At the restoration the College was among the many organisations and individuals who, whatever arrangements they had made willingly or unwillingly during the Interregnum, hastened to protest their disapproval of the Commonwealth regime and their delight at the return of the monarch. A new charter seemed to be needed to clarify the College's legal position.

At an audience with Charles II on 3 September 1660 President Alston – the same Edward Alston who had obtained the Cromwell charters – delivered an oration and gift of a unicorn's horn decorated with gold leaf, and was promptly knighted for his pains. As part of its campaign the College published a book by Dr Christopher Merrett outlining its legal powers and, to reinforce its reputation as a learned body, Merrett's catalogue of the library and museum.

The 1663 Charter of the 'King's College of Physitians in the Cittie of London' [see also page 26] confirmed the College's powers and made some constitutional changes 'with a profuse expenditure of words' (over 12,000 of them) according to Sir George Clark in the College official history. Legal disputes over the College's authority were to be resolved not by the common courts but by its 'Visitors', four high-ranking lawyers. However, Parliament declined to pass the bill that would have ratified this Charter.

James II Charter

In October 1685 the College learned that a writ of *quo warranto* was to be issued against the College Charter, requiring it to undergo a close legal examination. This was a device used by both Charles II and James II to ensure that the constitutions and ruling personnel of corporations and boroughs conformed to government policy. The College decided to surrender its Charter voluntarily and seek a new one. In its support the College issued a pamphlet outlining and justifying its legal powers. The new Charter, received in the College on 12 April 1687, affirmed and reinforced the College's authority over the apothecaries and the surgeons. It raised the limit on the number of Fellows from 40 to 80 – desirable for the needs both of the growing City and of College finances. It named all the Fellows, bringing in new ones that the regime favoured, several of whom had not experienced the education of traditional learned physic. In contrast, some established Fellows were omitted – Richard Morton for example, a former dissenting minister ejected following the 1662 Act of Uniformity. A division was created between the old and new Fellows, but a large section wished to retain the new Charter after King James's fall. Their bill to get this Charter confirmed in 1689 failed in Parliament and the College compromised by retaining both those Fellows introduced and those rejected by the Charter, except for a few well-known Catholics. It avoided further provocation, however, by not creating new Fellows for some years and allowing the numbers to dwindle.

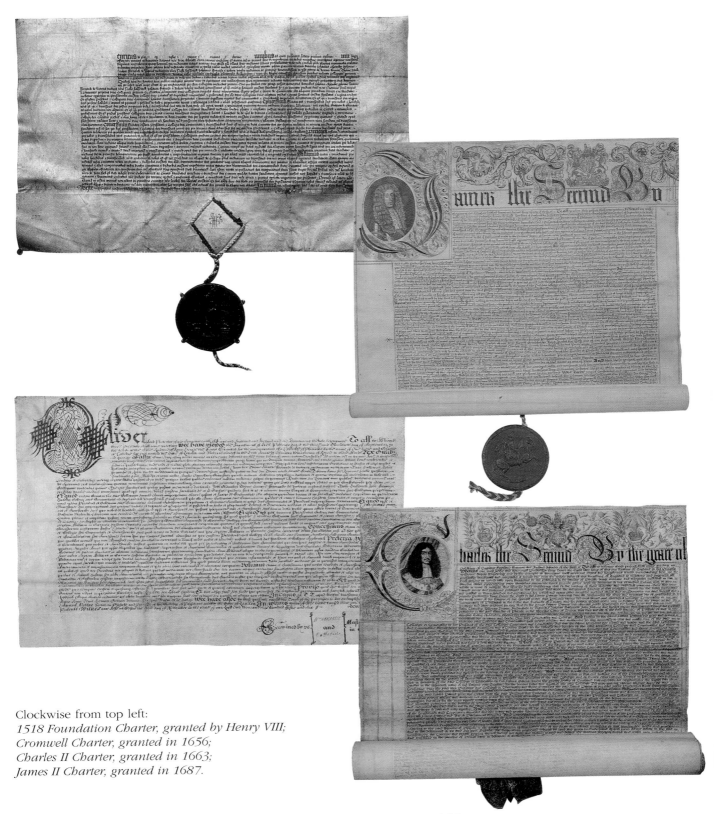

Clockwise from top left:
1518 Foundation Charter, granted by Henry VIII;
Cromwell Charter, granted in 1656;
Charles II Charter, granted in 1663;
James II Charter, granted in 1687.

Statutes

As early as the 1520s the College began to elaborate its constitutional rules by enacting statutes, or 'Statuta' (they were written in Latin), the forerunners of the bye-laws. (These are the 'statutes' referred to in this chapter and are not to be confused with the written laws of the land as established by Acts of Parliament, the more common meaning of the word.)

Dr John Caius, when President, produced the first consolidated edition, which incorporated all additions up to 1563 plus many of his own. He laid down the duties of the President and other officers, the procedures for their election, and elaborate rules of precedence. He went into considerable detail about the conduct of College examinations, appending a long list of books of which Candidates were required to know the contents, mostly the works of Galen of which he was a keen student. The only surviving text, a manuscript copy in the Bodleian Library, is printed as an appendix to volume 1 of Clark's history of the College published in 1964.

Reasons to amend these rules arose from time to time but a substantial revision, known as the Statuta vetera, was completed in 1601. It clarified the division between general meetings, normally held quarterly (Comitia majora), and Comitia minora or censoria, which met more frequently and to which most examining and disciplinary matters were delegated. It established the pattern of examining in three parts – physiology, pathology and therapeutics – that was to remain in oral or written form until 1867 [see page 44]. And, something that proved to be highly controversial over the years, it established a clear division between Candidates, destined to be promoted to the Fellowship after a suitable interval, and those who would remain Licentiates without a voice in the governance of the College [see pages 28, 33–4]. Matters of medical practice were also covered. Fellows were forbidden to venture

The 1647 edition of the College statutes, bound in red velvet with silver clasps and decorations, devised by Caius (below).

Bottom, left to right: King Henry VIII's coat of arms; the College coat of arms; the title page.

103

opinions on cases merely from the inspection of urine when they had not seen the patient.

Manuscripts of the next full revision, completed in May 1647, have survived intact and the official College version is still in the red-velvet binding, with silver clasps and decorations, which was devised by Caius for his edition. Changes of the previous 40 years were incorporated more systematically but without any radical introductions. Fellows had to be British and elects had to be English. It is clear from the wording on their diplomas that Fellows also had to be doctors of medicine from Oxford or Cambridge. However, an amendment of 1642 had made it possible for those who did not yet have such degrees to be elected as long as they undertook to obtain them subsequently. Others became and remained Licentiates, a division not abolished until 1835 [see facing page]. The Statuta moralia, the parts pertaining to matters of professional etiquette, were made more strict.

There was a strenuous effort to reinforce the College's authority following the granting of the new Charter by James II that introduced Fellows without the required Oxford or Cambridge education because of their political acceptability. Fifteen new statutes (the Statuta nova) were passed in 1688.

The new rules left former apothecary John Badger in a double bind. He passed the examination but was encouraged to wait until he got his MD, enabling him to be admitted as a Fellow rather than a Licentiate. When he returned with his doctorate he was told that the new regulations did not allow him to be admitted on a previous examination. He retaliated by getting a copy of the statutes from an ally in the College and publishing them with an English translation on the pages facing the Latin. This, he felt, would reveal to the public at large for the first time how unjust they were, an opinion shared by many at the time, and that the College charged people under regulations that it tried to keep secret.

How much the Badger case had to do with the proposal to translate the statutes into English in 1696 is difficult to say. Legal counsel supported the proposal but there was considerable opposition, partly it was said because the occasion was made a pretext to introduce stringent new fines for trivial offences. The English statutes were pushed through by the officers and were sealed without being read to the Fellows, resulting in a walk-out from Comitia by a number of Fellows in November 1696. These statutes stayed in force only till 1707.

During the eighteenth century there were amendments and revisions, particularly following Lord Mansfield's advice in 1771 after the revolt of the Licentiates [see page 34], but no radical alterations. The statutes were printed in 1745, though not for general circulation.

In 1811 the old Latin statutes were completely rewritten for the last time, and it was this version with minor amendments that was printed as an appendix to volume 1 of the report of the House of Commons Select Committee on Medical Education in 1834. The criticisms by this committee were no doubt the main stimulus to the reforms of 1835–6, although there had also been criticism in the medical press.

A campaign was conducted in the early 1830s in the pages of the *London Medical Gazette* by its correspondent 'Maxilla' (a pseudonym derived from the initials of Dr James Arthur Wilson). He referred to, among other things, the nonsense of a hierarchy based in effect on religious denomination rather than medical ability – a consequence of restricting the Fellowship to the Anglican Universities of Oxford and Cambridge was that religious dissenters could never rise above the status of Licentiate.

From late 1834 to early 1836 no Fellows or Licentiates were elected while the debate over the statutes took place. On 31 March 1835 the category of Candidate was abolished and with it the ruling about Oxbridge degrees. Instead all entrants to the College were to take the examination to become Licentiates. Fellows would be selected from among their number. Licentiates had to be at least bachelors of medicine and to have undergone five years of study and three years of hospital practice.

Along with these changes a standing preparatory committee, known as Council, was established to recommend Licentiates for promotion to the Fellowship and Fellows for various offices, as well as other business referred to it by Comitia. It first met in April 1836.

Campaigns for further reform within the College and in the medical profession at large during the first half of the nineteenth century suggested that further changes might be in the offing and probably explain why the College merely amended the 1811 version of its statutes after such a substantial reform. Several bills were presented to Parliament before the Medical Act of 1858 was passed. Thereafter the Licentiates became Members, confirming what they had often informally been called earlier.

The Medical Act suggested a new charter should be established so a Charter Committee was formed which met with representatives of the Edinburgh and Dublin Colleges (but not Glasgow) to discuss differences and to argue for amendments to the parts of the 1858 Act that they found unsatisfactory. This activity did not lead to a new charter, but the Charter Committee became the committee that revised the bye-laws and proposed most of the subsequent changes that took place.

The system of having eight elects to choose the President in secret was abandoned in favour of election by a majority of the Fellows present at the special electoral Comitia. The new licence was regarded as a first qualification, equivalent to a university MB, and one of several qualifications subject to the approval of the newly established General Medical Council. The system was introduced in the face of opposition from both legal and medical sources, including some Fellows. There were to be no more extra-Licentiates – there was no further point. The Latin statutes were abandoned and after all the debates were over the bye-laws were printed in English for the first time in 1862.

John Badger's publication of the College statutes, 1693, with a new English translation. Badger's aim was to show how unjust they were after he was refused admission as Fellow, despite having completed the required examination in 1683.
Right: *the title page.*
Far right and below: *an appeal to Parliament and an outline of his treatment by the College.*

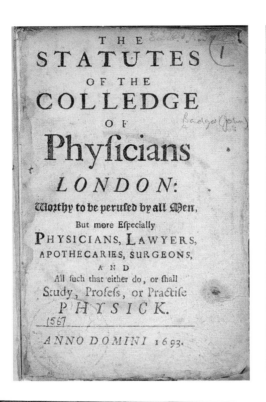

THE
STATUTES
OF THE
COLLEDGE
OF
Physicians
LONDON:
Worthy to be perused by all Men,
But more Especially
PHYSICIANS, LAWYERS,
APOTHECARIES, SURGEONS,
AND
All such that either do, or shall
Study, Profess, or Practise
PHYSICK.
1567
───────────
ANNO DOMINI 1693.

To the
PARLIAMENT
OF
ENGLAND.

MOST Renowned Assembly, whose Vigilancy and Care for the Publick Good, all Ages have sufficiently experienced, and in whose Determination the People of England, calmly, contentedly, and conscienciously acquiesce; tho the corruptions and perversions of ill men have frequently subverted your most Generous Designs for the Publick Good, to their own base and private Interests; among the number of which, it were heartily to be wish'd that the most Noble and Necessary Art of Physick were not prostituted and perverted (by men
        * 2.   strictly

strictly sworn to the contrary) to the avarice, pride, and oppression of a few, who not content privately to enslave and abuse men, by exacting Fourscore or a Hundred Pounds, for an Admission, without any Examination; but openly enact By-Laws, contrary to Act of Parliament and the Common Good of Mankind, precluding (without any respect of their Due and Legal Qualifications, and Abilities) particular men from being serviceable to the Publick; as will plainly appear to those who shall attentively examine the following Case, and Statutes. The prudent and seasonable redress of which Enormities, most Worthy Patriots, when time and opportunity shall present, is humbly submitted to your Determination and Judgement.

(1)

The Base, Dishonourable, and Illegal Dealing of the Colledge of Physicians, London, with a Doctor in Physick, admitted to that Degree in one of our own Universities;

WHo in July, August, and September, in the year 1683, presented himself to the President and Censors, to be examined; Doctor Thomas Coxe President, Samuel Collins, Senior Register, Walter Charleton, Thomas Allen, Nathaniel Hodges, Edward Hulst, Censors: and was by them examined (Chap. 15. pag. 112.) three several times in Latine, according to the Form of the Statutes (Chap. 16. pag. 119, 120, 123.) in that Case provided; and was approved (Chap. 15. pag. 111.) and had leave given by the President
    * 3   sident

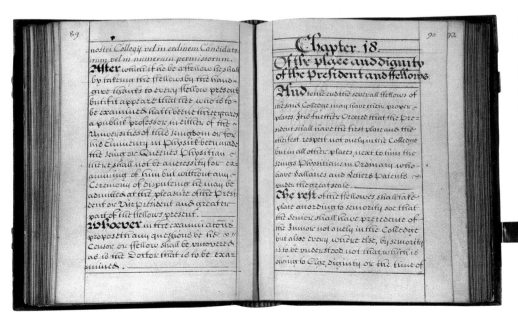

The College's own English translation of its statutes, 1696. These were arguably a stringent reaction to Badger's translation, were not approved by the Fellows, and were in force only until 1707.

Evening Meetings

In 1767, Comitia resolved to establish regular meetings for the reading of papers on various medical topics. A committee was appointed to organise them and to select papers for subsequent publication in a form similar to the *Philosophical Transactions of the Royal Society* [see page 54]. The first meeting was held on 22 June of that year and, as on all subsequent occasions, it took place from 9 p.m. to 11 p.m. and was presided over by the President.

A prominent member of the organising committee was the elder William Heberden who contributed the largest number of papers to the first three volumes of the College's *Medical Transactions* (1768, 1772, 1785). On 21 July 1768 he read a paper entitled *Some account of a disorder of the breast* (published four years later in volume 2), in which he gave the first description of the praecordial pain of myocardial ischaemia [see page 146]. He chose the word 'angina' (qualified by pectoris) to denote the characteristic 'sense of strangling' although formerly this term had conventionally been used to denote acute inflammation of the throat; Heberden himself had used it with that connotation in a paper describing an epidemic of an influenza-like illness that he read at an evening meeting less than a year before (*Transactions*, volume 1).

In 1785, for reasons that are obscure, both the evening meetings and the *Transactions* ceased and did not resume for another 21 years, when a second series of meetings began in 1806. Most of the papers selected for publication in volumes 4–6 of the *Transactions* (1813, 1816, 1820) were contributed by the younger Heberden, Matthew Baillie and John Latham.

Two papers were read by Sir Henry Halford, who became President in 1820. The meetings stopped again that year, probably due to Halford's preoccupation over the building of the College's new premises.

After their opening in June 1825, Halford lost no time in exploiting the College's new facilities and introduced a range of measures designed to strengthen its influence within the profession and to enhance its image in national life. Halford evidently had a high opinion of the value of evening meetings. Less than three years after the College moved, Comitia appointed a committee that included Pelham Warren and John Latham to revive the meetings in a form similar to those held in the past. From 9 p.m. to 10 p.m. papers were read, not by their authors, but by the Registrar or a senior Fellow, and they were followed by what was essentially a soirée for distinguished non-medical guests; references to 'mixed audiences' denoted the latter and not the inclusion of women.

The first meeting, attended by many notable figures of society, was held in April 1828, Halford reading a paper on tic douloureux. Evidence from the archives reveals that meetings were held regularly at least until 1832. During those years the names of authors and the titles of the papers which they submitted were recorded, though it is often unclear if the papers were actually read. In some cases correspondence between Pelham Warren and

Pelham Warren (1777–1835). Oils on canvas by John Linnell, 1836.

authors or members of the committee indicate whether papers were selected or not, but on most of the few manuscripts that have been preserved favourable or critical annotations have been made.

Comitia's original intention to resume publishing selected papers in a new series of *Transactions* was never fulfilled and papers were instead submitted to contemporary journals: several have been traced to *The Lancet* and the *London Medical Gazette*.

At first, this series of evening meetings was well attended, especially when Halford read a paper. Every year Comitia approved continuation of the meetings during the forthcoming season, but it may be significant that the archives contain nothing relating to authors or titles of papers after 1832. More ominously, in 1836, concern was expressed about poor attendance at meetings and Fellows were exhorted to support them and to submit papers. Evidently this was unsuccessful and there is no record of any evening meetings after 1838, though Comitia never made a formal decision to terminate them.

Among manuscripts that have lain unnoticed in the archives, one that was recently discovered is remarkable for several reasons. Entitled 'A few remarks upon the natives of Van Diemen's Land', it was read at an evening meeting in February 1829. Its author was a young man named John Barnes, who had not yet obtained a medical qualification but had worked as a medical officer in the Colonial Medical Service in Tasmania.

His paper gives a detailed medical and anthropological description of the Aborigines whom Barnes was able to observe closely only a few years before they became extinct. Many suffered from a dermatological condition that has never been described elsewhere; this was probably canine scabies caused by the Aborigines' intimate relationship to dogs that had been introduced to the island by the first white settlers, and were used by them and the Aborigines for hunting kangaroos.

Barnes was posted for 18 months as medical officer in charge of the notorious convict settlement in McQuarrie harbour. He was the sole medical witness at the Molesworth Select Parliamentary Committee on Transportation which met in 1838. During his evidence reference was made to his paper on the Aborigines and he stated that this was accompanied by illustrations which he had drawn. Unfortunately these have never been discovered; nor has his paper, which was recommended by Pelham Warren for publication, been traced to any journal.

John Latham (1761–1843). Oils on canvas by John Jackson, 1816.

6

Special Objects

The Caduceus

The College caduceus is the President's symbol of office and is carried on formal College occasions and when the President is representing the College. It is a silver rod, 68.8 cm long, with a plain disc at the base and moulded bands at graduated intervals, and capped by a beaker-shaped terminal supported by four curved snakes and inset with the arms of the College. The symbolism of the College caduceus is many layered, and whether or not the current debate that surrounds the interpretation of the symbolism was intended, it adds to its interest and significance.

It was devised by Dr John Caius and presented by him in 1556 and was first used on 10 January 1557 at the funeral of the Italian doctor Balthasar Guersie and then again at Caius' own re-election as President for a third year on 11 October 1557. Caius explained the idea and purpose of the caduceus in the *Annals* thus: 'The Caduceus or silver rod indicates that the President ought to rule with moderation and courtesy, unlike those of earlier days who ruled with a rod of iron. But the serpents, the symbols of prudence teach the necessity of ruling at the same time with prudence and the arms of the College placed at its summit indicate that these are the means by which the College is sustained.'

The caduceus, together with a specially bound copy of the statutes (and a cushion on which to carry it) and a seal, formed what Dr Caius called the *Insignia virtutis*, which he created as a means of introducing greater formality into College procedures [see also pages 98–9, 103].

In Greek mythology the caduceus was the wand carried by Hermes, the messenger of the gods who became the protector of travellers and merchants and ultimately trade in general, and thus became the symbol in the ancient world of heralds and ambassadors. The College caduceus differs from the caduceus of Hermes in having four snakes (which are not intertwined) at the top instead of two and in having the College arms embossed on the head instead of the wings which surmount the Greek god's staff.

Sir William Browne (1692–1774). Oils on canvas by Thomas Hudson, 1767. This is the most presidential of presidential portraits, with Sir William holding the caduceus, his other hand resting on the College statutes, while he wears his President's gown. He was President in 1766–7 during the revolt of the Licentiates (see page 36) and was satirised on the London stage by the actor/manager/author Samuel Foote in his play The devil upon two sticks. *He was a great defender of the privileges of the English universities. Garrulous and indiscreet, he is often seen as a buffoon, but he was a generous soul. After the dispute with the Licentiates he proposed his principal opponent, the Quaker physician John Fothergill, for the Fellowship (a majority of the Fellows voted against him). He congratulated Foote on his performance but after noting the absence of the muff he normally carried he sent him one of his own.*

111

The caduceus has now become widely accepted as a symbol of medicine, and has been confused with the longer-standing medical insignia, the rod and staff of Aesculapius with its single serpent. But in Caius's time, such confusion would have been unlikely.

Where did it begin? The visual similarity between the two is one obvious reason. Also, in the ancient world all staffs were viewed as symbolising the indestructible vitality of the earth. Thus the wand of Hermes, protector of the living, was essentially the same as the rod of Aesculapius that heals the sick and protects them from death, although in antiquity the caduceus was not associated specifically with medicine.

A likely route into medicine for the caduceus was through Hermes' association with alchemy and consequently chemistry as Hermes Trismegistus. As chemistry began to be used in the composition of medicines the caduceus appeared on the frontispieces of several seventeenth- and eighteenth-century pharmacopoeias.

However, the evidence does not support the view that Caius chose a caduceus for the College because he regarded it as a medical symbol. The alternative title of 'caduceator' that the Bedell was dubbed until the College was given a mace in the late seventeenth century [see below], reveals that originally it was he who carried the caduceus before the President, thus performing the function of his herald. Add to this Caius's known interest in visual symbolism that he acquired during his student days in Italy: he was likely to have been influenced by Andrea Alciati's book of emblems, which went through many editions on the Continent in the sixteenth century. This can be seen especially in his choice of devices for his own shield of arms, of which he left a careful explanation and which includes two serpents symbolising 'wisdome and grace'. And in 1558, after he had refounded his old Cambridge College, Gonville Hall, as Gonville and Caius College, he presented a caduceus to its master, similar to that of the physicians, with four serpents and a shield at the head, with the words: 'We give you the rod of prudent governance.'

We can be certain that he was fully aware of the history and symbolism of both the caduceus and the Aesculapian rod and staff. But by introducing the caduceus into the ceremony of the College of Physicians, Caius unintentionally added to the confusion between the two emblems for later times, when few people understand the visual signs with which he was so familiar.

The College Mace

The cup, which is surmounted by a royal crown, is embossed with demi-female figures supporting arcading above the emblems of England, Scotland, France and Ireland, and alternating with the monogram of Charles II, while on the cap are the royal arms of a Stuart sovereign. The hollow stave is in three divisions separated by acanthus-leaf chased knops (ornamental knobs). A small plain section below the cup is applied with three brackets, while the two larger lower sections of equal size are chased, with a spiral ribbon and similar tendrils bearing thistles, roses and other flowers. Acanthus leaves decorate the upper half of the foot-knop and underneath are the engraved arms of the donor and the College, together with the inscription: '*Hoc Caduceo Collegium Medicorum Londinensium Regale Johannes Lawson M.D., Eiusdem Socius Donavit Jan 1, 1683*'.

Dr John Lawson (before 1648 to 1705), an Arabic scholar, held several offices at the College before being elected President in 1694. His gift was acknowledged at Comitia on 24 March 1684 when he was described as 'a truly generous man' and 'a most worthy fellow of this illustrious college'.

This mace was a symbol of authority to be carried before the President, but originally a mace was a weapon made from non-precious metals with sharp blades, favoured by warlike medieval bishops for breaking armour. Initially the royal arms were placed on the lower terminal, but gradually they assumed greater significance and were surrounded by a coronet and later by a crown, by which time the mace was carried in reverse with the diminutive head now at the lower end.

The College mace is similar in design to the speaker's mace of the House of Commons after a pattern introduced by the London goldsmith, Thomas Maundy in 1649 when Parliament ordered all maces to 'bee made according to the same forme and patterne'. After the Restoration in 1660 many of these Commonwealth maces were not destroyed but their devices were removed and replaced by royal emblems and the design continued to be used until the late seventeenth century.

In selecting Anthony Nelme to supply his mace Dr Lawson chose a leading goldsmith who controlled a most successful London workshop from around 1680 until his death in 1723 at premises in Ave Maria Lane, when the College was near by in Warwick Lane.

As the College mace was a gift there is no record in the *Annals* of the cost. However, on 12 April 1684 the sum of £1 1s. 6d. only was entered in the cash book as a payment to 'Dr Lawson's man that brought his mace' confirming its arrival sometime previously. An indication of Lawson's munificence can be appreciated when it is realised that Maundy received a total of £146 11s. 8d., including the gilding, for the slightly larger House of Commons' mace of 1649. It is not certain whether the College example was originally gilt as the description '*virguleæ argentæ*' in the *Annals* remains inconclusive. The same workshop, however, made two maces in silver in 1697 for the borough of Bishop's Castle in Shropshire, and so the College example may have been supplied without the gilding in 1684.

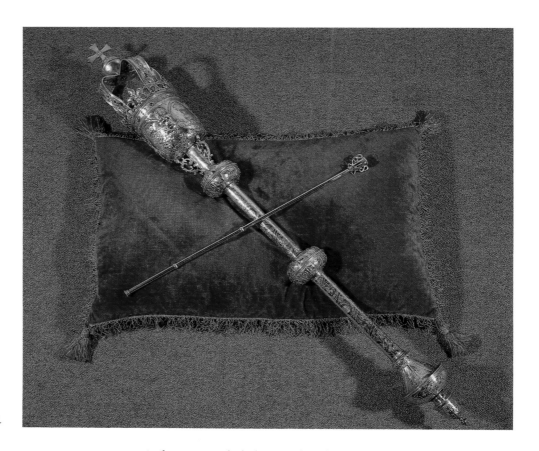

The silver caduceus, and the silver-gilt mace (137 cm long).

The Gold-headed Cane

The gold-headed cane, said to have belonged originally to Dr John Radcliffe (1652–1714), is a treasured possession of the College. For more than a century after the death of its first owner, the cane passed successively to five eminent Fellows, before the widow of Dr Matthew Baillie presented it to the College in 1825. The coats of arms of the previous owners, John Radcliffe, Richard Mead, Anthony Askew, William and David Pitcairn and Matthew Baillie on the cane's gold head were probably engraved together about the time when it came to the College.

Within two years of the College receiving this gift Dr William Macmichael, the College Registrar at the time, was inspired to write his book *The gold-headed cane*, in which an inanimate object tells its own story. The cane's charming 'autobiography', recounting its experiences in the company of eighteenth-century physicians and their patients, became a minor classic; the book also portrayed the gold-headed cane as an emblem of physicianly medicine of the period.

Dr William Munk, when editing the third edition of *The gold-headed cane* in 1884, gave the cane the opportunity to explain why its bar-shaped handle was unusual: 'The physician's cane proper has a rounded knob or head, often

114

of gold, sometimes of silver, but in later times generally of ivory. In earlier times this knob was perforated with holes, and it had within, a cavity or chamber, ... for aromatic or Marseilles vinegar ... of sovereign efficacy against all pestilences.' The College's decorative cane, however, is as one sees it, for nothing lies cunningly concealed in the gold head or in the malacca staff. The handsome cane was carried in conformity with contemporary fashions of dress and accoutrements rather than for medical purposes.

In contrast, ivory-headed pomander canes were often carried by doctors, apothecaries and quacks. Examples of the more commonly used dual-purpose medical canes are also included in the College collection. All varieties of medical canes and their owners were popular targets for carica-turists such as Hogarth and Rowlandson [see page 51] who used the cane as an icon to identify individuals with medical pretensions.

At the end of the eighteenth century the gold-headed cane remarked: 'I ceased to be considered any longer as a necessary appendage of the profes-sion.' The cane is *primus inter pares* both as an object of antiquarian interest and importance, as well as an elegant witness to a century and a half of College history and physicianly practice.

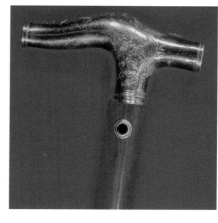

The top of the gold-headed cane.

Anatomical Tables in the Dorchester Library Gallery

The six seventeenth-century anatomical tables, in the Dorchester Library, were probably made by drying and mounting the actual blood-vessels and nerves of the human body on to thin blocks of wood and then varnishing them.

Johann Vesling (1598–1649), professor of anatomy at the University of Padua, has been suggested as the originator of this kind of teaching aid, that would doubtless have fallen into disuse soon after the introduction of spirit as a preservative. Any knowledge we have of their making is derived from the diaries of John Evelyn, who purchased four such tables in Padua in 1646. According to Evelyn they were the work of Dr Joanno Athelsteinus Leoncenae, presumably Joannes Leonius, called Estensis, Vesling's assistant from 1644 to 1649. Having extracted 'the veins and other vessels which contain the blood, spirits, etc., out of the humane bodies (which the many hospitals and infirmaries of that city [Padua] plentifully afford), [he] begun to apply and distend them on tables according to their natural proportion and position, as an improvement which might be of use for anatomy.'

The College set was formerly known as the *Tabulae Harveianae* because William Harvey was thought to have used them to demonstrate the circula-tion of the blood. However, if Harvey had done so, he would probably have presented or bequeathed them to the College, or at least have mentioned them in his will, and these six were not given to the College until 1823 by the tenth Earl of Winchilsea. Furthermore Sir Charles Scarburgh, Harvey's successor as Lumleian lecturer in the College, tried to persuade John Evelyn to give his set to the College in 1652 when Harvey was still alive, so Evelyn's were evidently the only ones that he knew about. Evelyn agreed only to lend them to the College to use for their anatomical lecture(s) and he gave them to the Royal Society in 1667. They were transferred to the British Museum in 1782 and finally to the Royal College of Surgeons of England in 1809, where they remain. Those four, and the College's six, are the only ones known to exist now.

There is a clue to the identity of the original owner and to the Harvey connection in a letter of 20 March 1665 from Dr Edward Browne, writing from Padua to his father, Sir Thomas Browne: 'The anatomy is done … 'Twas young Marchetti that dissected; hee first learned this dexterity of Sir John Finch … one that in anatomy hath taken as much pains as most now living. Hee hath tables of the veines, nerves, and arteries, five times more exact then are described by any author.'

Domenico Marchetti was Vesling's successor in the chair of anatomy at Padua. Sir John Finch married Elizabeth, a daughter of William Harvey's younger brother, Daniel. He graduated at Padua in about 1651 and became professor of anatomy in Pisa in 1659. He was admitted an Extra-ordinary Fellow of the College of Physicians in March 1661. Some years after his death, his favourite nephew, Daniel, took his uncle's belongings to Burley-on-the-Hill, the seat of the Earls of Winchilsea. (John was a younger brother of Sir Heneage Finch and the earldom is derived through the widow of Sir Heneage Finch's grandfather.) There is no doubt that Finch owned a set of anatomical tables (as Browne noted). More than 100 years after his personal property was taken to Burley-on-the-Hill such a set was found there, which makes it reasonably certain that the anatomical tables now in the Royal College of Physicians were originally Finch's.

In 1966 Gilbert Causey, professor of anatomy at the Royal College of Surgeons of England, identified the tables as far as he could. They are, reading from left to right, or south to north (in the Dorchester Library):

1. Nervous system.
2. Upper right specimen: portal venous system. Lower specimen: Professor Causey doubted its previous identification as the spleen and said hesitantly that it bears a marked resemblance to an injected placenta.
3. Arteries, where the heart is missing.
4. Veins.
5. Sympathetic nervous system.
6. Arteries.

Silver

The College strong room at Amen Corner was robbed when London was devastated by the plague and so few pieces of College plate pre-date 1665. Then the following year the building was destroyed in the Great Fire leaving little resources to replenish the losses while rebuilding was the priority. Fortunately the caduceus [see pages 111–2], Harvey's pointer and Hamey's bell are among the pieces that survived.

Baldwin Hamey (1600–76) was a generous benefactor to the College and held office there between 1640 and 1666. While acting as Registrar he used this bell to bring silence to Comitia and presented it to the College when he retired from the registrarship in 1655. Today the bell is still used by the Registrar at Comitia during the election of the President. The Latin inscription on the interior of the cast body: '*Mortuus est, tamen hic Auditur Hamaeus*' was added after Hamey's death in 1676. This small London-made inkstand bell of 1636 by an unknown master is believed to be the earliest surviving English hallmarked example.

A fortunate addition to the collection was made in 1914 when the College acquired through Crichton Brothers of Old Bond Street a salver on foot with London hallmarks for 1661 from the collection of Bertram, fifth Earl of Ashburnham. This fine piece, with its typical baroque embossed decoration incorporating beasts and birds, is engraved with two coats of arms and mottoes, those of the College and another – unidentified – suggesting that it once belonged to a Fellow and may have been stolen with the other pieces in 1665. The head of the porter's staff, recorded in the College cash book in 1679 when £8 7s. 3d. was paid to a goldsmith, Mr Robinson, and the College mace of 1683 [see pages 112–3] are the only other pieces that were added after the robbery that pre-date the generous gifts by College officers in 1719 and 1720. This is surprising because for about a century from around 1666 it was customary to present the President with a personal gift of plate weighing approximately 60 ozs. at the time of his election. No piece, even from the long presidency of Sir Hans Sloane (1719–35), appears to have survived.

In 1719 the four Censors, Hugh Chamberlen (1664–1728), John Freind (1675–1728), Richard Hale (before 1693 to 1728) and Richard Tyson (1680–1750) gave a punch bowl that today is used at the election of a President – no longer to hold punch but to collect the ballot papers. The following year the goldsmith Matthew Cooper I supplied ten candlesticks and a pair of snuffers and stands that were purchased by the Treasurer, Henry Levett (1668–1725) and the four Censors when Richard Mead (1673–1754) and Salisbury Cade (before 1688 to 1720) had replaced Chamberlen and Tyson.

Also in 1720, a silver-gilt standing cup and cover with the maker's mark of Edmund Pearce was given by John Freind to commemorate the renewal of the Harveian banquet, the year he delivered the Harveian Oration. The third gift received in 1720, an inkstand or standish with the maker's mark of Gabriel Sleath and weighing some 80 ozs., was presented by the Registrar,

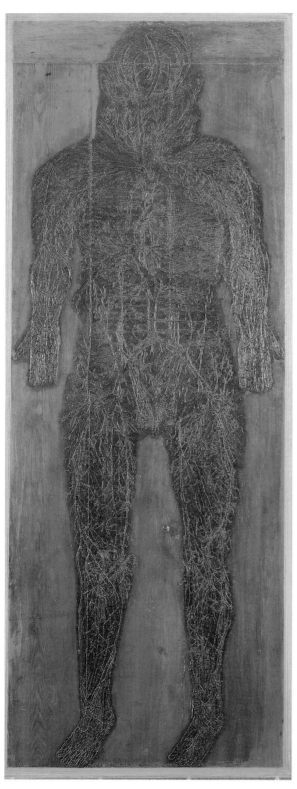

Four of the six seventeenth-century anatomical tables. Left: *veins;* right: *arteries.*

Left: *arteries where the heart is missing;* right: *nervous system.*

Hamey's silver bell, 1636.

Swiney Prize cup and cover, 1888, designed by Daniel Maclise. Awarded to Charles M. Tidy (1843–92).

Henry Plumptre (before 1697–1746) and completes this special group of fine-quality plate from the workshops of London goldsmiths. The pieces are in the native styles and show little of the Huguenot influence that was gaining popularity at the time.

During the nineteenth century it was traditional for a recipient of an honour from the Crown to give plate to the College, while other pieces were received as bequests. Following contemporary fashion large cups, drinking vessels and bowls were popular and many have contemporary inscriptions that remind us of past events. A cup in renaissance style, called the Fellows' Cup, records the names of all 55 Fellows in 1872 and 1873. Sir William Jenner's (1815–98) cup was given by his widow in 1902 and had been a gift from his grateful patient, Queen Victoria's eighth child, Prince Leopold, who suffered from haemophilia.

In 1938 Sir St Clair Thomson (1859–1943) gave a cup of 1789 that originally belonged to the eccentric but well-respected Edinburgh surgeon, Alexander Wood (1725–1807), who walked the streets accompanied by his pet sheep and a raven. In 1844 another Scottish doctor, George Swiney (c.1786–1844), died leaving a large bequest for a quinquennial prize of 100 guineas and a piece of silver of the same value for an essay on jurisprudence. The prize had to be jointly administered by the Fellows of the College and the Royal Society of Arts. Three of the cups that were awarded as part of this prize are in the collection, two after the original design by Daniel Maclise (1806–70) and the third by Melvin Oliver (1886–1958) from 1919 when the design was first changed. A further twelve new designs were used throughout the twentieth century, giving a chronological record of altering styles over 80 years. Dr Charles Mercier who received the award in 1909 and again in 1919 left both his cups to the College. The third cup in the collection, won by Charles Meymott Tidy in 1889, was presented by his son, Sir Henry Letheby Tidy, in 1953.

Among the small group of gold objects in the collection is the cane [see page 114]. Another piece, a late eighteenth-century three-colour gold bonbonnière from the Paris workshop of Toussaint-François Pillieux, played a similar rôle when it passed in turn to four Fellows from St George's Hospital, all of whom delivered the Harveian Oration. It was given to the College by the last owner, Dr William H. Dickinson (1832–1913), who was also curator of the museum for 16 years.

A gold-mounted rose-cut diamond ring was received from Dr Helen Dimsdale in 1972. This was originally one of many gifts received by Dr Thomas Dimsdale (c.1712–1800) from the Empress Catherine II after his first visit to Russia in 1768, when he successfully inoculated the Empress and her family against smallpox.

Some of the donations of the twentieth century include pieces by leading contemporary goldsmiths and have greatly enhanced the interest of the collection. Sir Samuel Squire Sprigge (1860–1937) left two champagne goblets designed and made by John Paul Cooper in 1911, a talented figure who was involved in the Arts and Crafts movement. Robert (Lord) Platt (1900–78) presented a dish by Leslie Durbin in 1959 during his presidential term.

Durbin's work is well known through exhibitions and public commissions including the altar plate at Guildford Cathedral and the sword of Stalingrad. An impressive centrepiece or rosebowl by another contemporary goldsmith, Gerald Benny, was a gift from Robert Alexander McCance (1898–1993) in 1962, while in 1986 Sheffield Fellows presented a dish in the form of a Tudor rose from the firm of Frank Cobb & Co.

Diamond ring given to Dr Thomas Dimsdale by Empress Catherine the Great of Russia.

In 1964, the year the current College building was opened, the physicians and surgeons of the Canadian College gave an interesting cigar box from the workshop of C. Paul Petersen. A native of Denmark, he worked with Georg Jensen before emigrating to Canada in the 1950s, settling in Montreal where he produced some exceptional hand-crafted items inspired by his original masters.

Another remarkable addition to the collection was received in 1957 when the American College of Physicians presented two salvers marking their first combined meeting in London that year. They are from the workshop of a Frenchman, Jean Simon Chaudron (1758–1846), who left France in the 1780s, and date from around 1810–15 while he was active in Philadelphia. Soon afterwards he moved with other French emigrants to Alabama where his descendants are still living.

The donations of plate to the College covering over 350 years have greatly enhanced its history and it is hoped the tradition will continue in the twenty-first century.

Medals

The College has a collection of over 100 different commemorative medals. Most have some connection with a notable person in the history of medicine and have a portrait on the obverse. They include strikes of some of the medals the College itself awards and a miscellany of medals from other medical organisations and congresses, British and foreign. Among them are examples of the designs of the best-known family of British medallists, William Wyon and his successors and a group of medals from the noted French school of the late nineteenth and early twentieth centuries.

Browne medal

Gold, in suspensory frame, by Thomas Pingo (*c*.1692–1776).

Awarded by Cambridge University on the instructions of Sir William Browne FRCP (1692–1774). Two gold medals were to be awarded annually for the best Greek ode in imitation of Sappho and the best Latin ode in imitation of Horace. The College also has two silver strikes. They were first awarded in 1775 and the inscription on the suspensory frame shows that this one was awarded in to H. H. Knapp for a Latin ode in 1803.

The medal was designed according to Browne's detailed instructions by Pingo.

Freind medal

Bronze, by Ferdinand de St Urbain (1658–1738), 1728.

John Freind FRCP FRS (1675–1728) as MP for Launceston from 1722 was asked in 1726 to present to Parliament the College's petition on the perils of cheap gin. An ancient and modern physician shake hands on the reverse of the medal, presumably an allusion to his *History of physic* (1726) which advocates a synthesis of old and new practice in medicine.

St Urbain from Nancy in France moved first to Bologna and then became head of Papal coinage in Rome, before returning to Nancy. In Italy he joined the Baroque school of medallists who generally produced their work by casting in bronze, rather than the more usual method of having them struck from dies. This is the College's only cast medal.

Kanthack medal

Bronze: obverse by Charles J. Allen (1863–1935), reverse by J. Herbert McNair (d.1955), 1900.

Awarded annually since 1900 to students in experimental pathology in Liverpool by Thomson Yates Laboratories, in memory of Alfredo Antunes Kanthack FRCP (1863–98).

Both Allen and McNair taught art in Liverpool. The same combination produced the Mary Kingsley medal for the Liverpool School of Tropical Medicine. McNair was a friend and former colleague in Glasgow of the architect Charles Rennie Mackintosh; he married Frances Macdonald, the sister of Mackintosh's wife, Margaret.

Moxon medal

Gold, by Allan Wyon (1843–1907).

Awarded triennially by the College from 1891 for observation and research in clinical medicine, in memory of Walter Moxon FRCP (1836–86).

Below: *the Browne medal, obverse and reverse.*
Below right: *the Freind medal, both sides.*

The reverse shows the façade of the College's fourth home in Pall Mall East, with the statues of Thomas Linacre, William Harvey and Thomas Sydenham sculpted in 1876 by Henry Weekes in the niches on the first floor.

The medal shown was awarded in 1939 to Sir Arthur Hurst (1879–1944).

The Symons Collection

Cecil Symons was a physician and cardiologist at the Royal Free Hospital, Hampstead, north London. His approach to collecting is best described in his opening to the Samuel Gee Lecture, which he gave at the College in 1981, entitled 'Invalids in the Georgian era'.

'I am not a medical historian but someone who became interested in the Georgian era because of the collection which I have made over the years of contemporary, primarily medical rather than surgical, instruments. The acquisition of articles may become a passion and arouse interest far beyond the particular inanimate piece collected. To see, for example, an early medicine spoon inevitably gives rise to thoughts of who used it and how and why. This will be the basis of my approach. I hope to show that the Georgians were very much aware of self-care and comfort and that even in sickness their inherent sense of good design remained evident.'

Although his main interest was in the Georgians, Symons did not limit his collection to one era or one country. Another theme was a comparison between the English and French approach to sickness and health in the eighteenth and nineteenth centuries.

During a College visit to Singapore in 1986, a year before his death, Symons told the then Treasurer, Sir Anthony Dawson, about his collection and how he would like the College to house it. However, there was no suitable site – until the new extension was being planned.

Below left: the Kanthack medal, obverse and reverse. Below: the Moxon medal, both sides.

Nipple shields: silver, ivory, lead, glass, ivory/wood/leather; and a glass milk expressor. Nineteenth century.

The architect, Sir Denys Lasdun, having seen items from the collection several years earlier, remembered particularly the nipple shields ('guards' as he called them), and designed the present exhibition space specifically to house the Symons Collection, enthusiastically supported by the Treasurer, Dr Norman Jones.

Until the collection arrived at the College, nobody had seen it in its entirety. The arrangement results from a combination of attempting to find a logical sequence that would both reflect Symons's interests and make a visual impact. As it was being arranged, people asked about the origins of the collection: when was it started, why were artefacts collected, where were they found? Initially, Cecil and Jean Symons collected a few objects because they liked them.

The first was an apothecary jar found in Chartres in 1957. In 1973, a silver 'top-hat' stethoscope was acquired but plans to collect silver stethoscopes were soon abandoned as there were no others to find. Other early acquisitions included a castor-oil spoon with a bottle of castor oil, a wooden stethoscope, a lancet case, an iron double-ended spoon (which turned out to be for kitchen use), a cupping set, and a tongue scraper (later identified as part of a Stilton scoop). Treen (wooden) cases containing medicine glasses and syringes, a pap-boat and a calibrated bleeding bowl, which was being used as an ashtray, were also added.

The development of the medicine spoon in the Georgian era, particularly the question of whether it preceded the teaspoon or vice versa, was of particular interest. In 1979, a spoon came up for auction inscribed 'Gift of the Dutchess of Queensberry to Lady Carbery'. Why did she give a spoon in a shagreen case? Was it for medicine or tea? She was known to have a deep interest in potions, tisanes and balsamic draughts and to have made them up for her friends. A dose of medicine became known as a teaspoonful and from 1755 when the Duchess gave her present until the recent introduction of the 5-ml plastic medicine measure the quantity had not changed.

Antique markets throughout England and France provided good sources of medical artefacts – especially as dealers had not yet realised their value – as did antique and junk shops in the USA and Australia.

Holidays and conferences provided opportunities to visit medical museums – the Medical School and Musée de L'Assistance Publique in Paris, Hospice de Beaune, Hotel-Dieu de Lyons, Semmelweis Museum in Budapest, museums in Vienna and Padua, and old hospitals in Piacenza, Siena, Florence, Angers and Bruges. Many English, Scottish and Welsh country houses also have items of medical interest.

The display begins with items from the largest group in the collection, 'invalid aids'. First, the nipple shields which also reflect Symons's interest in the variety of materials used to make the objects – in this case, silver, glass, ivory, wood, leather and lead (not good for babies). Modern examples have been included to show that although the material may have changed, the shapes have not. Next come items used for infant feeding, pap-boats, feeding cups and posset cups – including one with a removable handle and spout for travelling. A wicker-covered flask resembles an early thermos flask.

Feeding spoons form the next part of the collection: a magnificent example, the earliest in the collection (c.1680) is mounted high on the wall. Below it is a neat French invention – the medicine was in the first compartment with something sweet in the second.

Medicine and teaspoons are followed by castor-oil spoons. These are often called Gibson spoons because they were inscribed by the silversmith C. Gibson inventor; in fact, they were invented by Dr Anthony Todd Thomson (1778–1849) a Fellow of the College. Sick syphons are next. These are early drinking-straws which, being impossible to clean, were potentially lethal. Also in this part of the collection are double-ended spoons that were developed by the Victorians, and travellers' folding spoons, many of which came from America.

A magnificent William IV ear-trumpet that unscrews into three parts and could be carried in a handbag is displayed above the tongue scrapers, probably the largest collection anywhere. They fascinated Symons because of the variety of shapes and materials. A selection of items for dental care, including toothbrush sets, ends the 'self-care' part.

Next come items for leeching, bleeding and cupping, including many beautiful lancet cases in a variety of materials. A selection of stethoscopes includes examples of Laennec and Piorry models, an elegant Neapolitan model made of tortoiseshell and gold in its original case, and one made of glass. A sphygmographe de Marey that belonged to Sir William Broadbent is displayed and thermometers, pulsometers and tongue depressors are also represented.

The collection also includes a set of guinea scales (an important part of a physician's equipment), Chinese medicine dolls, a pair of political buttons showing Louis XIV having an enema – before and after – and a Charles I pillbox containing four divisions and a watch to show when the next dose is due.

Ear-trumpet: silver, 1833.

7

The Portrait Collection

The College portrait collection provides a pictorial and sculptural record of Presidents, Fellows (not all distinguished) and other physicians associated with the College from its foundation to the present day.

In 1596 the College resolved that any Fellow (or, it would seem, any outsider) could have his portrait hung on the payment of £10. To what extent this option was taken up is unknown, because almost all the early pictures perished in 1666 in the Great Fire of London, although the portrait of Harvey survived.

In the eighteenth and nineteenth centuries there was a deliberate policy of building up the collection by acquiring portraits as they became available and, since World War II, by commissioning portraits of Presidents. There remain some gaps in the earlier centuries.

The quality of the pictures varies but the collection is interesting not only as a record of the history of the College but also because it contains portraits by such major figures as Reynolds, Lawrence, Hudson, Hoppner, Zoffany and Millais. There are portraits by artists whose work is now largely lost, and also by unknown painters, of interest because they provide evidence about the standards to be expected in a given period from artists who were not in the front rank.

Judged as a whole the portraits tend to be formal, portraying the sitter as a serious physician, and sometimes displaying his academic credentials by his cap and gown. Presidents from the eighteenth century onwards often appear in the presidential gown together with other symbols of the office.

Portraits of the seventeenth and eighteenth centuries often contain indications of the interests of the sitter. For example the fine, although anonymous portrait of Sir Theodore de Mayerne (1573–1655), who also sat twice for Rubens, shows him holding a skull. This is probably not, as one might think, a *memento mori*, but signifies his contribution to the study of anatomy (he is said to have introduced a method for dissection of the skull). Whether or not it also refers to one of his treatments for gout that contained 'raspings of a human skull unburied' is uncertain.

Facing page: *Sir Theodore Turquet de Mayerne (1573–1655). Oils on canvas, artist unknown.*

He was born at Mayerne near Geneva and was named after Theodore Beza, the leader of the Protestant community in Geneva after the death of John Calvin. He was physician to King Henry IV of France and remained so until the latter's assassination in 1610 despite the Paris faculty's condemnation of his use of chemical remedies. He came to England in 1611 and became physician to James I and afterwards to Charles I.

126

Theodorus · Maverne · Eques · Auratus ,

Sir Charles Scarburgh (1614–94). Oils on canvas, artist unknown, c.1660.

A royalist in the Civil War, Scarburgh gained the friendship of William Harvey in Oxford. They remained friends and in his will Harvey left Scarburgh his velvet gown and 'all my little silver instruments of surgerie'. Scarburgh was physician to Charles II and left an account of the king's last illness. He had an excellent library, especially strong in mathematics. The painting was part of the contents of Temple Newsam, near Leeds, where it had presumably gone when Scarburgh's daughter married the 7th Viscount Irwin. It was bought and presented to the College by Dr R. W. Innes Smith in 1923.

The portrait of Sir Charles Scarburgh (1614–94) who was physician to Charles II, James II and William III, thought to be by Jean Demetrius, emphasises that he was also a distinguished mathematician. He published an edition of Euclid, and various Euclidian figures are depicted on the table at which he sits. The book on the table is open at plate II, Book II from Juan Valverde de Hamusco: *Vivae imagines partium corporis humani aeris formis expressae* (Antwerp, 1566), based on Vesalius. It shows the muscular system, presumably a reference to Scarburgh's book on the subject.

The portrait of Baldwin Hamey jnr. (1600–76) by Matthew(?) Snelling (one of the artist's few surviving works) tells us of Hamey's love of classical writers. He was 'the most munificent of all donors' to the College (Munk), and it is fitting that there is also a portrait bust of him by Edward Pierce which is regarded by Sir David Piper as 'the best [example] of English Baroque sculpture'.

Another important bust is that by Roubiliac of Richard Mead (1673–1754) commissioned posthumously by Anthony Askew (1722–74), another great collector. Mead commissioned Peter Scheemakers to create a bust of Harvey to replace the one lost in the Great Fire. The bust is based on one of two portraits of Harvey that Mead possessed.

In the Censors' room where the Roubiliac bust of Mead stands there is the portrait by Sir Joshua Reynolds of William Pitcairn (1711–91) who was President from 1775 to 1785. Pitcairn comes alive in the picture, as if he has been caught between one movement and the next and he seems to be on the verge of speaking. In the same room, against the Spanish oak panelling originally provided by Hamey for the Warwick Lane College, is the portrait of Thomas Sydenham (1624–89). Sydenham was not a Fellow, having taken his Oxford MD only 13 years before his death but such was his contribution to medicine with his emphasis on clinical medicine rather than theory that he was greatly esteemed by the Fellows of the College.

His portrait by (or after) Mary Beale is one of only a few in the College by women artists, another being by Mary Black (completed with help from her father) of Messenger Monsey (1693–1788). He, too, was not a Fellow, but an extra-Licentiate. He was first in practice at Bury St Edmunds, but Lord Godolphin, the son of Queen Anne's Lord Treasurer, having recovered from an attack of apoplexy while under Monsey's care, persuaded him to come to London. Here, Monsey's literary endowments and acuteness of mind secured him the friendship of many, including Robert Walpole and David Garrick. His manners nevertheless remained rough. He was physician to the Chelsea Hospital for some 50 years and died aged 96, having notified Mr Cruikshanks, the anatomist, that he would be dead in a few hours and inquiring whether or not it would be convenient for a dissection to be performed. It was.

The College collection has three portraits by Sir Thomas Lawrence: one of Matthew Baillie (1761–1823), pathologist, anatomist and physician (who attended King George III in his last illness); another of Sir Henry Halford (1766–1844), President for 24 years; and the third of Edward Jenner (1749–1823).

Baldwin Hamey (1600–76). Marble bust by Edward Pierce, 1675? Commissioned by the College for £50. Witnesses record seeing it in the sculptor's studio in 1675, but it seems to have remained there for some years. It may have been in the College by 1680, but the Cash book does not record the payment for it until 1684.

Richard Mead (1673–1754). Marble bust by Louis François Roubiliac. Though sculpted after Mead's death, the College Bedell George Edwards commended it for its presentation of Mead's 'real features'. Mead was a highly successful physician who declined the presidency of the College in 1744. He was one of the great collectors of his age – after his death the sale of his books lasted 28 days and sale of his pictures, sculptures, coins and other art objects similarly. According to Samuel Johnson, 'Dr Mead lived more in the broad sunshine of life than almost any man.'

Anthony Askew (1722–74). Statuette in unbaked clay, by Chitqua, c.1770. A Fellow in 1753, Askew was Registrar of the College 1767–74. Rare books and manuscripts acquired on his European travels as a young man formed the basis of a vast library which filled every nook and cranny of his house in Queen Square. After his death the sale of his library lasted 20 days. This is the only portrait of an owner of the gold-headed cane holding the cane. The sculptor was a Chinese artist who visited England in 1770–1 and, owing to the fragility of his works, this is the only certain example surviving.

Jenner, like Sydenham was not a Fellow of the College, although his work was admired by it. As a country doctor who had obtained his medical education mainly by apprenticeship, Jenner was not qualified to take the examination for the College Fellowship until Oxford University awarded him an honorary MD in 1813. A minor bye-law amendment in 1814 showed the College's willingness to admit him, but it felt unable to excuse him the usual examination, to be taken in Latin. At the age of 64 Jenner was disinclined to go to the trouble of brushing up his Latin to the necessary standard and so did not take the examination.

Parliament granted Jenner £10,000 in 1802 to reward him for his work on vaccination, and to compensate him for his expenditure in promoting the

William Pitcairn. Oils on canvas by Sir Joshua Reynolds, 1777.

130

Left: *Messenger Monsey (1693–1788). Oils on canvas by Mary (and Thomas?) Black, 1764.*

The artists are very little known. The sitter wrote to Mary Black thus, 'Sure I was bedevilled to let you make your first attempt upon my gracefull person ... drawn like a Hog in armour, or a poor melancholy poet in a Garrett ... as good luck would have it your father has taken it away to mend it or burn it'. Fortunately he did not burn it and it is impossible to say if he altered it much or at all. It was given to the College in 1877 by a donor whose family had it from Mary Black.

Right: *Edward Jenner (1749–1823) by Sir Thomas Lawrence, 1809.*

The portrait is of interest in that it seems that the head of Jenner had been originally painted on one canvas and then, at a later stage, inserted into another canvas, upon which the body and background were then painted. The reason for this is open to speculation. It may be that either Dr Jenner or Lawrence did not like the clothing and background originally given to him, and, rather than repaint, inserted it into a fresh canvas. Alternatively, the painting may have been damaged in some way at one stage in the nineteenth century: the head would have been saved and then a new body painted in for the doctor. Similar 'cut-out' heads have occasionally been found on other eighteenth- and nineteenth-century paintings so this is not unique.

131

*Edward Archer (1717–89).
Oils on canvas by Robert Edge
Pine, 1782.*

*Archer, a Licentiate of the
College, is portrayed inviting
the viewer in to the
Inoculation and Smallpox
Hospital in St Pancras. The
hospital moved to Highgate
later to make way for St
Pancras station. The image
this portrait projects of the
kindly physician contrasts
with the rather pompous presidential image of the College's
other full-length portrait in the
main hall, that of Sir William
Browne [see page 110].*

method of prevention. When a second grant was contemplated in 1807, Parliament asked the College to investigate the efficacy of the procedure. The College's report was strongly in favour; the communications it received in response to its request for information and opinions are now bound in three volumes as MSS 2319–2321. The portrait by Sir Thomas Lawrence was presented to the College in 1895 by William Hunter Baillie, the grandson of Matthew Baillie.

Another important figure in the history of inoculation was Edward Archer, a 'humane, judicious and learned physician' (Munk). His striking portrait hangs by the door leading to the offices of the President, Registrar and Treasurer. Archer is shown gesturing through a classical arch towards the St Pancras Inoculation Hospital to which he was devoted and in which, at his own request, he died in a specially prepared room. His portrait by R. E. Pine was paid for by the governors of the hospital and in his will Archer recompensed each of them with the amount of his contribution.

William Hunter (1718–83) teaching anatomy at the Royal Academy. Oils on canvas by John Zoffany, c.1775.

Hunter was obstetrician to the aristocracy and ran an anatomy school in Great Windmill Street. He was the first teacher of anatomy to the Royal Academy of Arts on its foundation in 1768.

133

Main picture: *Sir Richard Quain (1816–98). Oils on canvas, by Sir John Everett Millais, 1896.*

Quain, born in County Cork, was on the staff of the Brompton Hospital from 1848. He is best remembered for his Dictionary of medicine *(1882 and 1894). In the College he was Senior Censor and Vice-President and was President of the General Medical Council from 1891 until his death.*

Below: *Millais's portraits of Benjamin Disraeli, 1881* (below), *and William Ewart Gladstone, 1879* (bottom), *in a similar pose.*

A picture of special interest is that by Zoffany depicting William Hunter (1718–83) demonstrating anatomy at the Royal Academy. Sir Joshua Reynolds is recognisable in the audience, holding his ear-trumpet.

The portrait of the physician Richard Quain (1816–98) by Millais makes a curiously familiar impression. Quain is shown in the same stance as Gladstone, Disraeli and Henry Irving in the portraits that Millais did of them. The portrait of Quain is believed to be the last that Millais painted.

Among the twentieth-century portraits, those of Viscount Dawson of Penn (1864–1945) by Philip de Laszlo and of Lord Moran (1882–1977) by Annigoni are particularly fine. Dawson's authority and Moran's cunning are evident. There is a story (unverifiable) that when Sir Winston Churchill (who was Moran's patient) saw this portrait he said: 'Just right Moran: makes you look like a mediaeval poisoner.'

Two Presidents of the second half of the twentieth century are represented in busts: Lord Brain (1895–1966) by Sir Jacob Epstein, and Sir Raymond Hoffenberg by Dame Elisabeth Frink. Both are good likenesses and that of Hoffenberg conveys tellingly a sense of his strength and determination.

In addition to the paintings and sculptures, the College has some 4,500 engravings and prints of important figures in the history of science, medicine and literature, especially of the late seventeenth to nineteenth centuries.

Rt Hon Bertrand Edward Dawson, Viscount Dawson of Penn GCVO KCB KCMG MD FRCP (1864–1945). Oils on canvas by Philip de Laszlo, 1937.

His Cavendish lectures of 1918, elaborated in the report of the Ministry of Health's Consultative Council on Medical and Allied Services which he chaired, put forward plans for a comprehensive health service. Although prominent among his proposals, the 'health centre' did not feature in the original NHS plans, but the idea was adopted by some of the new towns of the 1950s and has since developed as general practitioners have seen the advantages of cooperative practice with ancillary services.
As President of the College 1931–8, Dawson secured the election of a number of younger Fellows and encouraged them to take part in College affairs. He formed committees to review recent developments in research and medical education and believed that the College should co-operate with other royal colleges in such matters.

Above: *Sir Raymond Hoffenberg. Bronze head by Dame Elisabeth Frink, 1990.*

Walter Russell Brain, 1st baron Brain of Eynsham (1895–1966), PRCP 1950–7. Bronze bust by Jacob Epstein, 1958.

8

Personalities

Thomas Linacre (1460?–1524). Oils on panel, copied by William Miller from a painting at Windsor Castle. This is the usually accepted image of Linacre although the earliest record of the original from which it was copied appears in James II's catalogue where it is called 'An old man'. The name of Linacre had been attached to it by 1734 but the date and provenance are unknown and the date on the scroll is in dispute – it may be later than Linacre's death. The copyist was the College Bedell.

William Harvey (1578–1657). Oils on canvas, artist unknown. Formerly attributed to Cornelius Johnson, Sir David Piper in the College's Portraits catalogue says, 'It is certainly not from his hand'. Painted from life or possibly just posthumous, it was one of the treasures saved from the fire of London in 1666 and is one of the authentic likenesses identified by Sir Geoffrey Keynes, from which several versions are derived. Piper was also positive that the right hand had been damaged and restored, but a conservator examining it under x-ray in 1998 could see no evidence of any alteration.

William Harvey (1578–1657). Oils on canvas by Robert Hannah, 1848.

A nineteenth-century romantic view of Harvey demonstrating his theory of the circulation of the blood to King Charles I.

Below left: Baldwin Hamey (1600–76). Oils on canvas by Matthew(?) Snelling, 1674. A rare example of a work by this obscure painter.

Below: Daniel Whistler (1619–84), artist unknown, c.1660/70.

Right: *Sir Hans Sloane (1660–1753). Oils on canvas by Thomas Murray, c.1725.*

Below: *title page of the first volume of Sloane's natural history of Jamaica.*

Below right: *an advertisement for Sloane's milk chocolate.*

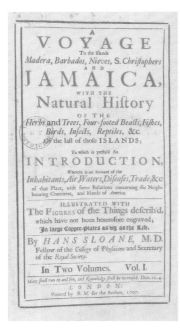

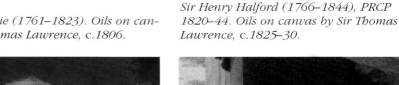

William Heberden (1710–1801). Oils on canvas from the studio of Sir William Beechey – a copy of Beechey's original of c.1796.

Sir Henry Halford (1766–1844), PRCP 1820–44. Oils on canvas by Sir Thomas Lawrence, c.1825–30.

Matthew Baillie (1761–1823). Oils on canvas by Sir Thomas Lawrence, c.1806.

Far left: *Sir William Withey Gull (1816–90). Painted wooden relief plaque by John Brooke Nash, 1937(?).*

Left: *Gull by Spy, with notably less stern demeanour.*

Below left: *Charles McMoran Wilson, 1st Baron Moran of Manton (1882–1977). Oils on board by Pietro Annigoni, 1951.*

Below: *Robert Platt, Baron Platt of Grindleford (1900–78). Oils on canvas by Merlyn Evans, 1963.*

Thomas Linacre (1460?–1524)

Thomas Linacre was a highly respected scholar in the humanist tradition. The term 'humanist' is a nineteenth-century one but *'studia humanista'*, a passionate interest in and close study of ancient literature and the stylistic imitation of ancient Latin authors, developed in Italy during the fourteenth century and was an essential feature of the Renaissance.

The early proponent of this kind of study, Petrarch (1304–74), established moral reform as the guiding principle of humanism, despite the inevitable tension between the pagan tradition and Christian doctrine.

In the fifteenth century humanists concerned themselves with the process of translation. They rejected the earlier word-for-word methods based on the assumption that words were originally assigned to specific things and reflected a cosmic reality, and attempted to render the broader sense of an original Greek text in elegant Latin. The techniques of textual criticism and the methods of working to establish authentic texts developed by this school were later applied to Biblical studies, most notably by Erasmus of Rotterdam, the leading humanist scholar of Linacre's time. Erasmus not only sought Linacre's medical advice, but also described him as having uncommon literary judgement.

Linacre wrote two Latin grammars: *Rudimenta grammatices* (in English despite its Latin title) and *De emendata structura latino sermo* (in Latin). He studied Greek under the best teachers of his time: Cornelio Vitelli in Oxford and Demetrius Chalcondylas in Florence – later teaching Greek to Sir Thomas More. His stay in Italy, lasting possibly for six years, included visits to several cities. In Padua he graduated MD at the university and met the Venetian printer, Aldus Manutius, whom Linacre assisted on a translation of the works of Aristotle; Linacre received praise for the high level of his scholarship in the preface to the second edition.

Linacre's reputation rests mainly on his translations into Latin from original Greek manuscripts of six works of Galen at a time when several scholars were attempting to satisfy the desire to return to the original medical texts which had been transmitted through the Middle Ages in Arabic versions. He was considered to be an accurate scholar, meticulous rather than imaginative.

He was physician to two monarchs (Henry VII and Henry VIII from his accession) and to other notables of his time: Princess Mary (1496–1533), Richard Fox (Bishop of Winchester), Archbishop Warham and Cardinal Wolsey. He was also chosen as tutor to Prince Arthur and later to the future Queen Mary I. This was the scholar physician who was able to persuade his king that the kind of medical organisation to be found at the time on the Continent would be advantageous to the welfare of the English common-wealth and thus the College was born.

140

William Harvey (1578–1657)

William Harvey was born in Folkestone on 1 April 1578 and attended King's School, Canterbury. He became a student at Gonville and Caius College, Cambridge, and in 1600 moved to the University of Padua where he graduated doctor of arts and medicine on 25 April 1602.

Harvey moved to London later in 1602, became a Candidate of the College in 1604 and a Fellow in 1607. Thereafter he was an active participant in College affairs. He was elected a Censor three times – in 1613, 1625 and 1629 – and became an Elect in 1627 after Sir Theodore de Mayerne declined the office because of his duties at Court. He was chosen as Treasurer in 1628 and 1629, but resigned from the office only two months after his re-election in 1629 in order to accompany the Duke of Lennox on his continental travels on the king's instructions.

He was appointed Lumleian lecturer in the College [see page 40] in 1615 and in 1616 began his lectures that he continued intermittently for 40 years. There were interruptions when he went abroad, both the journey of 1629–30 and one in 1636 with the Earl of Arundel's embassy to the German emperor in 1636 as well as, more seriously, the break in the 1640s caused by the Civil War. He eventually resigned in 1656.

Harvey, along with Sir William Paddy, was chosen in 1625 to consult the Lord Mayor of London over the prevention and treatment of the plague. His great gift to the College was the estate of Burmarsh in Romney Marsh, by which in 1656 he endowed the annual oration and feast and the honorarium of the Harveian librarian. The library and museum, known as the *Musaeum Harveianum* and containing Harvey's books were added to those already accumulated from the time of Linacre onwards. It was opened in February 1654 [see page 70]. The trust deed urges the Fellows to continue in mutual love and affection among themselves for the honour of the profession and the dignity of the College. Later in 1654 Harvey was elected to the presidency, but declined the offer on the grounds of his age and infirmity.

Harvey was physician to St Bartholomew's Hospital from 1609, although royal duties interrupted his work there. He was appointed physician-extraordinary to Kings James I and Charles I and eventually physician-in-ordinary to the latter, whom he followed to Oxford and the battle of Edgehill during the Civil War, returning to London after the fall of Oxford to the Parliamentary forces in 1646. Charles I encouraged his researches and gave him access to his deer at Hampton Court for his experiments.

Harvey's understanding of the circulation of the blood must be seen in relation to the period he spent at the University of Padua. There the modern study of human anatomy had begun with the work of Vesalius [see pages 81–2] and continued with that of Realdo Colombo. Colombo's *De re anatomica* (1559) included a description of the movement of the blood from the heart through the lungs and back and is cited by Harvey. Harvey's teacher, Hieronymus Fabricius ab Aquapendente, published a description of the valves in the veins without fully understanding their action, and their function became one of the keys to Harvey's understanding of the circulation.

It was only in 1628, 26 years after his graduation at Padua, that Harvey published his description of the circulation in *Exercitatio anatomica de motu cordis et sanguinis in animalibus* (An anatomical disputation on the movement of the heart and blood in animals), generally known as *De motu cordis*.

The movement of the heart is an important part of Harvey's thesis – the demonstration that the main action of the heart is that of pumping out the blood during the systolic phase rather than drawing it in – was contrary to what was generally believed. Another significant finding was his measurement of the volume of blood leaving the heart in a given time – far too much to be used up by the body and replaced by blood manufactured in the liver from chyle produced from ingested food, as the Galenic physicians would have it.

Exactly when Harvey's views on the circulation crystallised cannot be said for certain. Some of the lecture notes he wrote at the beginning of his period as Lumleian lecturer have survived in the British Library and have been transcribed and translated by Gweneth Whitteridge, who found statements that are incompatible with the ideas put forward in *De motu cordis*. It seems unlikely, therefore, that the discovery had been made as early as 1616.

However, in his 1628 preface addressed to the President and Fellows of the College, Harvey said of the circulation, 'Having now, however, for more than nine years confirmed it in your presence ...'. This would indicate that by 1619 he had arrived at some of the ideas that formed his anatomical system and was able to demonstrate experiments to his peers and gain their opinions, but he continued to experiment in order to confirm his hypothesis.

His discovery was accepted and even praised by some Fellows in the College soon after the publication of *De motu cordis*, according to James Primerose, Licentiate in 1629 (Harvey was one of his examiners), in the introduction to his 1630 book in which he attempted to refute Harvey's theory. It remained a theory until Marcello Malpighi described the capillaries as seen through a microscope in 1661, as Harvey did not have a lens powerful enough to enable him to see exactly how the blood moved from the arteries to the veins.

His hypothesis was opposed by one of the leading anatomists of the time, Jean Riolan, the younger, of Paris, to whom Harvey published two essays in reply. Harvey also had met Caspar Hofmann (a Padua graduate) in Altdorf, Germany in 1636 and tried to persuade him of the truth of his ideas. But Hofmann objected, partly on the grounds that he could not understand how the blood moved from the arteries into the veins, but also because he could see no purpose in the blood's constantly circulating round the body. Harvey recommended these physicians to repeat his experiments and see for themselves. The circulatory system was for him something to be made clear to the senses by the anatomical methods he had learned in Italy.

Harvey also had a lifelong interest in embryology, a subject also studied by his teacher Fabricius: notes about generation in deer and hens appear in the 1616 lecture notes and in *De motu cordis*. By the time Sir George Ent saw Harvey's notes, probably in 1648, he had accumulated a mass of facts and observations, including a few on the circulation in the foetus. He concluded that all animals grew from some kind of egg, but for technical reasons at that period he was unable to develop a complete theory of generation. *Exercitationes de generatione animalium* was published in 1651.

From the time of Harvey onwards the College has been disposed to encourage the application of scientific investigation to the advancement of medicine as well as promoting high standards of patient care. This follows the example of his work as well as the words of exhortation in the trust deed for the library and annual oration 'to search and study out the secrets of nature by way of experiment'. His elucidation of the motion of the heart and the circulation of the blood around the body of an animal have a significant place in the intellectual movement now generally called the 'scientific revolution'.

Baldwin Hamey, junior (1600–76)

Perhaps the most generous benefactor of the College of any Fellow, Baldwin Hamey was born in London, the son of Baldwin Hamey, senior, an immigrant from the Netherlands and former physician to the Tsar of Russia. He was brought up in the Calvinist tradition of the Dutch Reformed Church in London, of which he was still a member in 1640, and had numerous patients in the parliamentary party although he subsequently became an enthusiastic royalist.

His nephew, Ralph Palmer, later wrote that he sent donations of money to Charles II during his exile and he made gifts for the repair of the old St Paul's Cathedral and other Anglican churches. His generosity extended to the school and university expenses of a particularly deserving scholar.

Hamey studied philosophy and medicine at Leyden University, and graduated in medicine and incorporated his degree at Oxford. He became a Fellow of the College of Physicians in 1634. He served as a Censor eight times, was Registrar 1650–4, leaving for the use of his successors the silver bell with which he called Comitia to order [see pages 117–8], and Treasurer 1664–6.

In 1651 the building at Amen Corner then occupied by the College was liable to confiscation by the Commonwealth authorities as Church property – it was rented from St Paul's Cathedral. Dr Hamey bought it and gave it to the College. His donations towards the building in Warwick Lane including £100 towards the purchase of the ground (equal to the President's contribution), £50 for the wainscotting in the Fellows' meeting room (now in the Censors' room at St Andrews Place) and several other gifts amounted to £502 6s. 8d. in all. In 1672 he gave to the College Ashlyns Farm in the parish of High Ongar, Essex. It was sold in the 1920s.

Daniel Whistler (1619–84)

Daniel Whistler was elected a Fellow in 1649 and was a Censor twelve times between 1657 and 1680 and Registrar several times between 1674 and 1682. In Munk's Roll it is stated that he 'in an evil hour was elected President in 1683' – the basis for Munk's concern is described later. Whistler died in office on 11 May 1684 at the age of 65. He had earlier been a Fellow of Merton College, Oxford, a member of Gray's Inn and Professor of Geometry at Gresham College. He was a successful physician in London and is mentioned favourably in the diaries of Pepys and Evelyn [see also pages 26–7].

He is best remembered as the author of the first printed description of rickets in his thesis for the degree of Doctor of Medicine, presented in Leyden in 1645, entitled *De morbo puerili Anglorum quem patrio idiomate indigenae vocant The Rickets*. Many copies of this thesis still exist in English libraries. A translation from the original Latin text was made by Geoffrey Smerdon and published in 1950. The thesis was presented four years before the publication by Arnold Boote of his monograph *Observationes medicae de affectibus omisissis*. In chapter 12 of that book rickets is described and there is now an English translation of that chapter in the College library. In 1650 Francis Glisson and colleagues presented their lengthy and substantial report on rickets to the College. That report was published in 1650 in Latin and reprinted in English the following year.

Remarkably, the condition was well known to the general public before it had been described in the medical literature. Death from rickets is first recorded in the bills for mortality for the City of London in 1634 and the original report is still to be seen in Guildhall Library in London. In that year 14 deaths were ascribed to rickets in the City and by 1660 there were 521 cases. John Graunt in his *Natural and political observations* in 1666, covering the period from 1629 to 1660, suggested that in the bills of 1629 rickets may have been listed under the heading of 'livergrown'. That conclusion was based on talking to the lay people who made the diagnosis for the bills.

Sir Norman Moore, President of the College of Physicians 1918–22 in three publications (one of which was his own MD thesis and another was his entry for Whistler in the *Dictionary of National Biography*) denigrated Whistler. He thought Whistler guilty of plagiarism and thought he was dependent on Glisson's efforts. Clearly, however they were both describing something that had already been recognised by those who were not physicians and they were simply codifying the condition.

But Munk's criticism of Whistler was not just because of his doubts over Whistler's clinical authority, but also stemmed from the fact that the College lost money while Whistler was in office. Recently, Alec Cooke examined in detail the problems and wrote 'there is little doubt that both Moore and Munk criticise Whistler on slender and in places non-existent evidence'. It is to Whistler's credit that his thesis for the degree of Doctor of Medicine is still quoted 350 years after it had been submitted.

Sir Hans Sloane (1660–1753)

Hans Sloane, born in Northern Ireland, came to London in 1679 under the guidance of Robert Boyle, the chemist, to study botany and physic. He completed his studies in France, gaining his MD from the University of Orange. While a live-in assistant to Sydenham he became FRS in 1685 (for botany) and FRCP in 1687. To Sydenham's disgust he left for Jamaica as physician to its new governor, the Duke of Albemarle. The reason for Sydenham's opposition is not known, but one year later the Duke was dead and Sloane came home, escorting the mad Duchess and his collection of animals. Encouraged by John Evelyn, he wrote his classic description of the island in 1707.

He became an effective Secretary of the Royal Society, married a rich widow and settled in Bloomsbury in 1695. He started at the top, being created a baronet in 1716 for his services to royalty. His huge practice included 16 dukes and 10 earls, yet every morning he treated the poor for free. A sceptical physician, he was an enthusiast for quinine and smallpox inoculation. At the College and the Royal Society he was a great facilitator of other people's work and unique in combining the presidency of the College (1719–35) and the Royal Society (1727–41).

Sloane corresponded with Boerhaave, Linnaeus and Voltaire. He knew everyone of consequence. Locke and Halley were close friends. He calmed Newton's neurosis, helped Pope build his grotto and showed Handel his manuscripts. When his house needed repair he asked Wren to look at it. He was a good companion. Pepys wrote to him 'almost wishing myself sick again that I might ... invite you for an hour or two by yourself'. His unfailing support of John Ray, the ailing and impoverished botanist, was an example of true friendship.

Sloane retired to his manor of Chelsea, bought by him in 1702 and where he gave land for the physic garden. There he sorted out his huge collections, for he was the greatest collector of the century and intimate with his fellow collectors. He proposed to leave all his collection to the nation provided that the government would build a museum to house it. Soon after his death the government fulfilled his wishes, raised money from a lottery, and built the British Museum as a permanent memorial to Sloane.

William Heberden, the elder (1710–1801)

William Heberden was the son of a coachman turned Southwark innkeeper who died when William was seven. A scholarship enabled him to go to St John's College, Cambridge, in December 1724 and there he remained until he moved to London in 1748, eventually becoming MD, a Fellow of St John's and tutor in medicine. Among his students were two future Presidents of the College, (Sir) George Baker and Thomas Gisborne.

In 1740 he instituted a series of lectures on materia medica and it was in this field that his influence was first felt in the College of Physicians. He made careful studies of the composition and effects of medicaments, in so far as that was possible with the limited knowledge of chemistry at that period. He also rejected previously accepted ideas like the doctrine of signatures whereby the colour or shape of a drug or plant supposedly indicated its usefulness. Samuel Johnson called him 'Ultimus Romanorum, the last of our learned physicians', but he took a critical approach to the ancients, especially their knowledge of drugs.

When the College was in the process of revising its pharmacopoeia, he printed for circulation among the Fellows his pamphlet on Theriac or Venice treacle, demonstrating its mythological origins, its frequently changing composition over the centuries and the error of assuming that some 60 ingredients could act together effectively. Although some of his ideas were incorporated into the 1746 revision, Venice treacle was retained until the next revision in 1788 – no doubt because older patients would have expected it.

In 1746 Heberden was elected a Fellow; he was later a Censor three times, a consiliarius and an Elect 1762–81. He delivered the Goulstonian and Croonian lectures and was Harveian Orator in 1750. In 1767 Heberden's plan for the College to publish a journal was adopted and the first volume of the *Medical Transactions* appeared in 1768 [see page 54]. He was one of the most regular contributors and it was here that some of the clinical descriptions for which he is best remembered were published – the first clear description of 'angina pectoris' or ischaemic heart disease and his careful differentiation of chickenpox and smallpox. His *Commentaries on the history and cure of diseases*, published after his death by his son, William, contained numerous other such descriptions, including the now eponymous nodes on the finger joints in osteoarthritis. Although he was not certain of their significance, he was able to dismiss any connection with gout.

His concern was not solely with individual patients, however. He published anonymously a collection of London bills of mortality, pointing out their limitations as a means of discerning trends in population numbers and the incidence of diseases, and recommending that there should be a register of births, diseases and deaths.

The subtitle of his descendant Ernest Heberden's biography of 1989 aptly describes him as 'a physician of the Age of Reason'.

146

Matthew Baillie (1761–1823) and Sir Henry Halford (1766–1844)

Matthew Baillie first studied in Glasgow before attending Balliol College, Oxford, where he graduated MD. In London, soon after graduation, he became assistant to his uncle William Hunter in his anatomy school in Great Windmill Street, and shortly afterwards was his joint successor. His clarity and intelligibility made him a successful medical teacher there for nearly 20 years.

This faculty stood him in good stead as a physician: his explanations to patients and relatives of the problems, treatment and likely outcome of an ailment were clear, to the point and devoid of technical terms. Despite his Scottish manners that could make him appear blunt at first, his style made him successful in consulting practice.

His reputation was made by the publication in 1793 of *The morbid anatomy of some of the most important parts of the human body*. Collections of post-mortem findings had appeared in print before, notably by Morgagni in 1761. But Baillie's work was the first to be organised systematically under the organs of the body, concentrating on the lesions essential to the disease being studied, in order to relate better the findings after death with the clinical picture during life. He continued to add to his observations and four expanded editions were published during his lifetime. He was thus in the forefront of medical thought in his day, developing a method of investigation that was taken up by others such as Richard Bright [see pages 90–2] and was widely applied later in the nineteenth century.

How much his researches benefited his own practice as opposed to the knowledge and ideas they gave future diagnosticians is impossible to say. Nevertheless, an indication of his demand as a physician is his income for consultations that at the height of his career from 1810 onwards regularly exceeded £8,000 and even reached £10,000. King George III appointed him one of his physicians-extraordinary in 1810, but he declined that monarch's offer of a baronetcy.

In the College he served as a Censor twice and became an Elect in 1809, but resigned in 1818, to the regret of President John Latham, who had hoped Baillie would be his successor. In 1819 he gave his large collection of anatomical and pathological specimens together with a sum of money for its maintenance. He bequeathed his library of some 900 volumes [see page 72], a working library in which only a small percentage of the books would have been regarded at the time as antiquarian, though in retrospect it reflects the medical developments of his day. The College's copy of the first edition (1819) of Laennec's *De l'auscultation médiate* for instance came with the Baillie library.

Sir Henry Halford was born Henry Vaughan, the son of Dr James Vaughan, a physician of Leicester and was educated at Rugby School and Christ Church, Oxford. With his Oxford connections and pleasing manners he was rapidly accepted in London society and married the daughter of Lord St John of Bletsoe. By 1793 he had been appointed physician-extraordinary to the king and in the end was physician-in-ordinary to four monarchs in succession from George III to Victoria.

When Lady Denbigh, the widow of his mother's cousin, Sir Charles Halford, died in 1809 and left him a large fortune, he changed his name by Act of Parliament to Halford and was created a baronet in that year. His ability as a diagnostician is shown by the story of his views on the illness of Georgiana, Duchess of Devonshire in 1809. He alone of all the physicians consulted attributed her condition to an abscess of the liver and Dr Baillie's post-mortem examination revealed that this was indeed the problem.

His published papers are generally on topics that concerned practising physicians of the time. 'On the necessity of caution in the estimation of symptoms in the last stages of some diseases', read at the College in 1820, emphasises the need to inform the family and friends of the patient where a fatal termination may be expected. If not, the grief of the family might be increased by the thought that the physician had possibly been taken by surprise and had failed to do all that might have been done to prevent the death. He undoubtedly had the bedside manner that suited his patients and an ability beyond that of most of his contemporaries to apply the medical knowledge that had been gained up to that time to the care of his patients.

In the College it was Halford who succeeded John Latham in 1820 and he was re-elected President each year until his death in 1844, the longest-serving individual in that office by far. This led to the implication in *The Lancet*, then the new radical medical journal under the editorship of Thomas Wakley, that he regularly conspired to restrict access to the top posts in medicine to the élite he favoured. Readers of *Private Eye* might compare the series of 'Intercepted letters' that he had supposedly written to friends and published by *The Lancet*, to the fictional 'Dear Bill' letters written by John Wells during the Thatcher premiership.

Due to Halford's royal connections the list of guests at the opening of the new College in Pall Mall East on 25 June 1825 is a hugely impressive catalogue of princes, dukes, members of the government, and other notables. That morning the Royal Guelphic or Hanoverian order was conferred on Halford (KCH, promoted later to GCH). Yet, as noted in the introductory chapter to this book, despite his evident social and medical conservatism one of the most significant changes in the history of the College occurred during his presidency: the ending of the restriction of the Fellowship to Oxford and Cambridge graduates.

Despite their different origins and contrasting approaches to medicine, Baillie and Halford held each other in the greatest respect as doctors. In his last illness it was Halford's advice above all that Baillie sought. Halford's obituary oration on Baillie reveals his admiration particularly for his generosity of character and his sagacity as a physician. By that time also he had evidently begun to see the potential usefulness of Baillie's pathological researches. Both, of course, had undergone a classical education at Oxford. Both regularly attended George III and were equally baffled along with everyone else of the time by his periods of mental aberration.

The two physicians were also painted by the leading portraitist of the day, Sir Thomas Lawrence, though Halford in a grander manner as PRCP and GCH. Halford's portrait is also made more impressive by being in one of the wide, elaborate frames that Lawrence favoured. Although no maker's name is visible on it, frame experts recognise it as the type made by George Morant, Lawrence's frame-maker in the 1820s.

Sir William Withey Gull (1816–90)

William Gull was a man with an outsize personality, and by the end of his life he had amassed a fortune to match. He was of humble origin, being the sixth and youngest son of a bargee and wharfinger in Thorpe-le-Soken in Essex, who died only a year after Gull's birth. However, his talent, fostered by the teaching of his mother, came to the notice of the local vicar who happened to be acquainted with Benjamin Harrison, the influential Treasurer of Guy's Hospital, which owned land near by. Harrison took Gull to London and obtained a post at Guy's for him, where, after a period as a school-teacher, he qualified in 1841.

His rise was rapid and at first he taught physiology and natural philosophy, his companion as joint Fullerian Lecturer at the Royal Institution being Michael Faraday, and he was elected FRS in 1869. He was appointed to the staff of Guy's as assistant and then full physician in 1851 and 1858. A major event in his career was the attack of typhoid suffered by the Prince of Wales in 1871 (the same disease had killed his father, Albert). Gull was called in late when the outlook seemed grave, and the Prince recovered: the grateful Queen made him a baronet and retained him as her physician.

Gull's contributions to medicine as a scientist-physician were many, and although he was not the first to describe anorexia nervosa it was he who brought the condition to a wider audience: 'savages explain, science investigates'. He discovered myxoedema, was an expert on diseases of the spinal cord and with Henry Sutton (1836–91) made a major contribution to the study of the arterioles in hypertension and nephritis. A lesser-known contribution was to promote the pioneer epidemiological study, *The collective investigation* of 1882. His teaching and writing were impressive and aphoristic, his speaking style that of a seasoned and effective orator.

His clinical epigrams were much quoted: '"I do not know" is manly – if it does not stop there', and his scepticism of the use of many medicines well

149

known: 'Medicines do most good when there is a tendency to recovery without them.' He was reported to be kind and considerate to his patients and diligent in his duties, visiting the ward with a frequency unusual in contemporary physicians. His notebooks reveal a complex, sensitive, thoughtful and well-educated man.

He was elected FRCP in 1848, giving the Goulstonian lectures the following year, and later was a Censor, giving the Harveian Oration in 1870. However, the other side of Gull's personality, his dogmatism and assertive manner, brought him twice into conflict with colleagues which involved the College.

The first concerned the notorious 'Balham Mystery' of 1876. This infamous incident involved the death of a young lawyer, Charles Bravo, from antimony poisoning. A murky sexual background, involving his wife's liaisons before marriage and relations with Dr James Manby Gully famous for his water cure, death by poisoning, possible murder and an unknown protagonist, all conspired to make the 10-day inquest a national event.

The matter was complicated by the fact that Bravo was George Johnson's patient. Johnson (1818–96) of King's College Hospital was Gull's and Sutton's bitter opponent in the matter of the arteries and blood pressure in nephritis. Gull was also called as a witness in court and made comments on the conduct of the case that were publicly and bitterly disputed by Johnson, so that Gull referred the case to the College Comitia for adjudication. Comitia however ruled in favour of Johnson. Gull apologised icily and thereafter broke with Johnson.

The second conflict, in 1880, concerned a patient of his colleague at Guy's, Frederick Pavy (1829–1911), and occurred during the 'great nursing dispute' at Guy's which undoubtedly polarised opinion. The patient had died after a bath forcibly administered by a nurse, and Gull – although he had never seen the patient, nor the post-mortem – expressed strong opinions at the trial of the young nurse for manslaughter that Pavy's management of the patient had been deficient. Gull was reprimanded in the medical journals, but an enquiry by the College dubiously exonerated both Pavy and Gull.

Despite these incidents, Gull is remembered as one of the great British physicians of the nineteenth century.

Charles McMoran Wilson (1882–1977), 1st Baron Moran of Manton

As a junior doctor at St Mary's Hospital, London, in 1910 Dr Charles Wilson was appointed editor of the hospital *Gazette*. In July of that year he wrote an editorial on the 'national control of all those things which concern the public good ... In that category come the various hospitals. It is not our intention to enter into the right or wrong of their control by the State. That this control is coming there can be no manner of doubt.'

Clearly Aneurin Bevan's solution to the organisation of the former voluntary and municipal hospitals in the 1940s, that of nationalising them, would not be a surprise for Moran. He also voiced the concern for 'the influence of character on the medical student', for which he was later noted as Dean of the Medical School. In this respect he was a great believer in the virtues of rugby playing but whether because of – or despite of – this approach, he was also responsible for reviving the academic fortunes of the St Mary's Hospital Medical School. His contemporary, the surgeon Sir Zachary Cope, gave the relevant chapter in his history of the medical school the title 'The great dean – Lord Moran (1920–45)'.

Moran wrote *The anatomy of courage* that, although not published until 1945, is based mainly on his experiences as a regimental medical officer in the trenches of World War I when he was awarded the MC. Its three sections are titled: 'The discovery of fear', 'How courage is spent' and 'The care and management of fear'.

Moran was elected a Fellow of the College in 1921. Apart from joining the team of examiners for the Membership in 1933, he did not take an active part in College affairs during the presidency (1931–8) of Lord Dawson of Penn, although he shared the latter's desire to restore the College's influence in the nation's medical affairs. His 'Note on policy' of March 1938, his first serious intervention in College affairs, was a typescript document of 16 pages circulated to Councillors and a few other Fellows. In it he set down what he believed was wrong. One example was the failure of the agendas of Comitia (the general meeting of Fellows) to provide any opportunity for the discussion of current matters of importance, such as the introduction of clinical units into the London medical schools, a development he had been intimately concerned with at St Mary's. His solution was the development of a more active and more democratically elected Council.

In July 1938 he was elected Treasurer, and it was the College's lack of involvement in the emergency arrangements after the outbreak of war that led to his election as President in 1941.

This was a crucial period for the College, as planning for health services in the post-war world was initiated at an early stage. Sir William Beveridge's report on *Social insurance and allied services*, with its assumption that there should be 'comprehensive health and rehabilitation services for prevention and cure of disease and restoration of capacity for work, available to all members of the community,' appeared in 1942.

Serious discussions on the future shape of Britain's health services got under way shortly after that. Moran was especially assiduous in opposing the British Medical Association's desire to establish its right to speak for the whole profession, asserting instead the right of the royal colleges to organise, to speak for and to negotiate for their consultants. His letter to Sir John (later Lord) Stopford in 1943, though no doubt overstating the case, reveals his attitude to the question clearly: 'I believe it would be disastrous for the country if the BMA are (*sic*) allowed to run the consultants. ... We shall go to the Ministry to demand 2/6 extra pay, not to insist on proper standards.'

From early 1944 Charles Hill (later Lord Hill of Luton) became Secretary of the BMA and the mutual suspicion and antagonism between him and Moran became a feature of relations between the BMA and the College. Moran regarded Hill as devious, and many in the BMA felt the same way about Moran. It was probably they who nicknamed him 'Corkscrew Charlie'.

Although the BMA in 1930 had proposed a general medical service with access for 'every member of the community', it opposed the 1946 National Health Service Act owing to the fear of its GP members that it would lead to their becoming salaried servants of the state. For Moran's contrasting approach of constructive criticism see 'The College and the NHS' [pages 57–9].

Another issue that troubled Moran was the number of GPs who also practised as consultants in non-teaching hospitals. In his maiden speech in the House of Lords on 1 June 1943 he looked forward to the time 'when everyone is able to obtain the services of a consultant who has had proper training' and told of 'towns with a population of 100,000 where major surgery and everything else is done by general practitioners. All this must end: it is one of the greatest evils of our time in the medical world.'

In the end he achieved his stated aim of the 'gradual eliminating of the GP consultant' (1943 letter to Lord Stopford again). Around the time that Moran gave up the presidency he took on the chairmanship of the Standing Advisory Committee on Distinction Awards. The Spens committee on the remuneration of consultants was set up in 1947 partly as a result of Moran's pressure for a body similar to the one that had reported on the payment of GPs in 1946. Its recommendation that individuals should be differentiated for 'exceptional reward in respect of outstanding professional ability' – one-third of all specialists – reflected Moran's views as a Committee member. He regarded this work as one of his important achievements, although it had its critics from the beginning.

It is as Winston Churchill's personal physician that he is best known outside the medical profession. During World War II, when he had to accompany the Prime Minister to conferences overseas, he regretted that he was unable to be in the College more frequently. He is, however, known not only for his treatment of his eminent patient, but also for the revelation of his infirmities, published in 1966 in *Winston Churchill: the struggle for survival 1940–1965*. Although the people around Churchill knew Moran was keeping a diary and felt that some kind of memoir ought to be published at some stage, they were surprised when a book with so many personal details appeared so soon after its subject's death. Several of them complained that they had been quoted without permission. Most of the medical profession was appalled that clinical details of a patient should be published in this way. An 'Annotation' in *The Lancet* of 23 April 1966 was categorical in its condemnation: 'that Lord Moran, by writing publicly about the medical condition of an identified patient, is creating ... a bad precedent which none should follow.'

However, it was undoubtedly fortunate that the College had someone with Lord Moran's determination to ensure that its voice was heard in government circles, and in the medical profession at large, at a time of significant changes in health service provision.

Robert Platt, Baron Platt of Grindleford (1900–78)

There have been many distinguished Presidents of the Royal College of Physicians. However, with the possible exception of Lord Moran, Robert Platt was to be the most influential of any twentieth-century President. He was Professor of Medicine in the University of Manchester when he succeeded the London neurologist, Lord Brain, and was the first President to break the stranglehold of the London consultants on one of the highest offices in British medicine.

Platt was also the first full-time professor to become President, setting a precedent that has been followed by all the eight Presidents who have followed him. More than anything, he transformed the College from a somewhat stuffy institution occupying inadequate premises in Pall Mall East to a dynamic organisation housed in a new building in Regent's Park, that was opened by HM the Queen in 1964 [see pages 66–9]. The new building was a modern development designed by the exciting young architect, Denys Lasdun.

Platt also had a major influence on the College report on *Smoking and health*, published in 1962 [see pages 57–9], arguably the most important contribution that the College made to improving health during the twentieth century. It was Platt who inaugurated the College's postgraduate conferences when it still resided in Pall Mall. He also held important views on undergraduate medical education, serving as a member of Lord Todd's Royal Commission on Medical Education where he strongly stressed the importance of exposing medical students to general practice, as well as encouraging such so-called 'soft' subjects as epidemiology and the social sciences.

Born in London, he went with his parents to Sheffield, where he graduated MB ChB in 1921 (with two gold medals). He became MRCP in 1925, and FRCP in 1935. As physician to the Sheffield Royal Infirmary he acquired a successful private practice. He served in the RAMC during the war, ending it as brigadier, sometimes described as somewhat bedraggled. Service life did not attract him and it was after the war, in 1946, that he turned to the world of academe and became Professor of Medicine in the University of Manchester. There he studied renal disease and hypertension and built up an outstanding department that included such distinguished members as Douglas Black (later Sir Douglas and future President of the College) as well as Malcolm D. Milne, who became Professor of Medicine at the Westminster Hospital and Fellow of the Royal Society. Undoubtedly Platt's major interest outside medicine was music and he was himself an accomplished cellist.

A strong supporter of the NHS, Robert Platt had socialist leanings. In later life, as a cross-bencher in the House of Lords, his views were less consistent because he opposed the compulsory wearing of seat belts. Although he himself had been a successful professor in Manchester, he deeply offended his fellow academics in his notorious Harveian Oration in 1967, attacking them for their concern with unimportant rare diseases instead of concentrating upon psychiatric illness, drug treatment and other things that he considered to be of central importance to the practice of medicine.

After his death it was said that: 'In any medical generation there are a few who are recognised by a wider public not merely as great figures in their profession but as men or women of stature in the world beyond it...' In all that he did for his profession and for the College, his influence was immense.

Appendices

GLOSSARY

JULIE BECKWITH, COLLECTIONS LIBRARIAN, AND GEOFFREY DAVENPORT

Persons – Officers and Membership

Assistant Registrar / Academic Registrar
The first Assistant Registrar took up the post on 5 March 1883. The evolution of this office into an independent one dealing with conferences, research fellowships and awards was reflected in the change of title to Academic Registrar when Humphrey Hodgson became the 18th holder of the post in 1993.

Candidate
A person who had passed the examination to become a Fellow. In the days when the number of Fellows was fixed by Statute, a Candidate had to wait for a vacancy caused by a death or a resignation. Later he underwent a one-year probationary period. The category was abolished in 1835.

Censor
Four Censors were specified in the foundation Charter to assist the President in examinations and disciplinary matters. Elected annually 'to enquire about all practitioners of medicine … to examine, correct and govern them, if necessary to prosecute them …' All the College's examinations were conducted orally by the President and Censors until the 1830s. They were joined by three Pro-Censors in 1974 and now serve for two years. They were until 1998 ex-officio members of Council. The six Censors are now ex-officio members of the Education, Training and Examinations Board, of which the Academic Vice-President (Senior Censor) is Chairman.

Consiliarius
Adviser or counsellor to the President; for some two and a half centuries from the foundation of the College the Elects selected two of their number annually as consiliarii by themselves.

Elect
The 1523 Act of Parliament that ratified the foundation Charter charged the six persons named therein with choosing two others to form the 'Elects'. Thereafter they selected one of their number annually *in camera* as President and selected replacements to join their oligarchy of eight following deaths or resignations. This system was ended by the Medical Act, Royal Colleges of Physicians 1860.

Fellow
Full members of the College, constituting its governing body through Comitia (see below) until 1994; from 1995 an annual general business meeting has replaced the quarterly meetings. Until 1835 doctors of medicine of Oxford or Cambridge were examined by the Censors as Candidates for the Fellowship. From 1836 to 1859 Council proposed suitable Licentiates for election to the Fellowship; since 1860 Fellows have mainly been Members, proposed and elected by existing Fellows, although bye-laws now allow distinguished non-Members to be elected.

Honorary Fellowships are bestowed on persons not holding a medical qualification who have rendered exceptional service to medicine.

Hans Sloane Fellow
Responsible for international relations since 1986.

Harveian Librarian
The Fellow elected to supervise the College's library and information service. (Note: Librarian was from 1959 to 1997 the title of the information professional appointed to run the library service.)

Licentiate
Until 1835 all graduates of universities other than Oxford or Cambridge underwent a similar examination to the one taken by candidates for the Fellowship, but were not able to vote in Comitia, to which they were sometimes summoned for special purposes. From 1836 to 1859 all entrants to the College membership took the postgraduate examination for the Licence, with the possibility of promotion to the Fellowship after four years.

In 1859 the Licence became an undergraduate qualification, similar in standard to a university bachelor of medicine.

Linacre Fellow
The office was created in 1965; the holder is responsible to the President and Council for all matters relating to the general professional and the higher specialist training of doctors.

Member
From 1859 the normal mode of entrance to the College ranks has been through the postgraduate examination for the Membership. Since the early 1970s the examination has been conducted jointly with Edinburgh and Glasgow physicians' colleges for the MRCP(UK) [see page 23] and holders of this diploma may apply to become 'Collegiate Members' of the London College. Members of at least four years standing are eligible for election to the Fellowship.

President
The President is required to be a prudent person, skilled in the science and practice of physic and one who has been a Fellow for at least ten years. He or she is elected by all the Fellows, annually on the day after Palm Sunday, in theory without limit to the number of re-elections, but convention has recently restricted the term of office to five or six years. Before the establishment of the offices of Registrar and Treasurer the President carried out the bulk of the administrative work. (For the earlier system see Elects above.) The President has power to summon meetings of Council; the boards and committees and can refer to Council such business as is appropriate.

Registrar
Established in 1579, he was to attend Comitia and other meetings and to record 'all the discussion and decisions made by the President and the agreement of the majority' – he began to do so in 1581. In the year 2000 he or she is secretary to Council (see below) and is now responsible for all matters concerning the membership generally, the regional activities of the College, elections and appointments within and by the College and the appointment of physicians under the terms of the relevant regulations.

Treasurer
In 1566, the Annals record the first use of an account book. In 1583 the College elected its first treasurer, who took over from the president the duties of receiving all revenue, looking after College property, making provision for repairs of the building, paying salaries, dealing with prosecutions and lawsuits and preparing statements of accounts. A Finance Committee was set up in 1873.

Vice-President
Named pro-president in the earliest Statutes of 1555–63. Arrangements for appointments to this office have varied over the years. In 1964 the arrangement was introduced whereby the Senior Censor is Senior Vice-President and a Second Vice-President is elected separately. From 1992 to 1996 there was also a Paediatric Vice-President. Since 1999 the College has an Academic Vice-President and a Clinical Vice-President.

Committees and Boards

Boards

Four boards to undertake preparatory work for Council were proposed in 1990 and established in 1991; they were the Censors' Board (continuing the Censors' supervision of examinations and other educational matters), a Clinical Standards Advisory Board, a Finance and General Purposes Board and a Paediatric Board (the latter disbanding after the paediatricians formed their own Royal College in 1996). Since 1999 there have been six boards, named the Clinical Affairs, Communications and External Affairs, Education Training and Examination, Finance and General Purposes, Medical Specialties and Professional and Regional Affairs Boards. (See also 'Comitia minora' in the next section.)

Comitia

The meetings of Fellows were known from earliest times as Comitia – the general meetings Comitia majora, the meetings of the Censors variously as Comitia minora, Comitia censoria or the Censors' Board. The Statutes specified quarterly meetings for Comitia majora and these continued until 1994, although extraordinary meetings could always be called for urgent or important business. Originally all Fellows were expected to attend Comitia majora unless they could show good reason for their absence. Comitia minora (or Censors' Board) met more frequently, often apparently *ad hoc* as business presented itself, but eventually settled down to a quarterly event preceding full Comitia (see also Censor above). From 1995 an annual general business meeting has replaced the quarterly meetings.

Council

In 1682 a standing committee, known simply as 'The Committee' was formed, consisting of the four Censors, the treasurer and five others. It's duties included the preparation of the agenda for Comitia. In 1836 Fellows thought the College needed '… a better system for the general government of the College …' and a new standing committee was established. Soon known as Council, its remit was to deal with any business referred to it by full Comitia. In practice it became a standing preparatory and executive committee. Since the ending of quarterly Comitia meetings in 1994 and their replacement by an annual general meeting, Council has become the governing body of the College.

Staff

Bedell

The College has had a bedell (or beadle) at least since 1556, given the alternative titles of 'Bedellus' or 'caduceator' in the earliest Statutes. From 1691, when the language of the records changed from Latin to English, 'bedellus' became 'beadle' and then around 1840, for reasons not recorded, the College adopted the antique spelling of 'bedell', otherwise used only in Oxford and Cambridge universities. In addition to his ceremonial duties the College's beadle, like most of his kind, was a summoner, calling members and officers to meetings, candidates and empirics to be examined by the Censors. From 1711 until the end of the 19th century he also looked after the library. In 1904 the College Lists begin to name the post 'Bedell and Secretary', although one correspondent addressed the Bedell as 'Secretary' as early as 1841. In effect, he had been the College Secretary probably from the sixteenth century, the only administrative staff the College required for about three and a half centuries. The most recent change in the Bedell's duties occurred in the late 1980s when, following the leasing of the houses in St Andrews Place, the College decided it needed a specialist buildings maintenance officer, a function previously included among the Bedell's duties.

Secretary

It was not until Horace Barlow was succeeded as Secretary at the end of World War II by Miss Ina Cook that the secretarial functions were separated from the ceremonial and household maintenance functions. The title was changed to Chief Executive in the late 1990s.

College Lists from the 1940s onwards reveal a steady increase in the numbers of other administrative staff until they currently number around 140.

ROYAL MEDICAL COLLEGES AND FACULTIES

Because the organisations now designated 'Royal Colleges' have been established in different ways it is not easy to establish an order of priority. They all now have in common a royal charter, but this has sometimes preceded the attachment of the epithet 'royal' to their names. Collegiate status has in some cases been acquired before a royal charter (Royal College of Obstetricians and Gynaecologists, Royal College of Pathologists and the Royal College of General Practitioners, although the latter got the royal before the charter). The RCP of London was a college with a royal charter long before the 'royal' was added to its name. The first to have a royal charter was the body now known as the Royal College of Surgeons of Edinburgh, although at the time it was a small group of barber-surgeons in a small part of what now constitutes the city of Edinburgh. But despite the RCS of Edinburgh's seniority in respect of its chartered status it is fair to claim that the Royal College of Physicians of London was the model for other such organisations.

The Colleges and their Faculties, including the nursing Colleges, are listed below in order of their acquisition of a collegiate status or of a royal charter, whichever came first.

1505   Royal College of Surgeons of Edinburgh
Barber-surgeons of Edinburgh founded 1 July 1505 by 'Seill of Cause' from the City; confirmed by Royal Charter (King James IV), 13 October 1506.

Charter of 'Royal College of Surgeons of the City of Edinburgh', 22 May 1778 (Geo.III).

1518   Royal College of Physicians of London
Founded by Charter of Henry VIII, 23 Sept. 1518 as 'President, College or Commonalty of the faculty of medicine in London'); confirmed by Parliament 1523.

Acts of Parliament 1858 and 1860 accepted 'Royal College of Physicians of London' as the usual name but left it open to change.

Royal College of Physicians of London Act 1960 finally confirmed this name legally.

1599   Royal College of Physicians and Surgeons of Glasgow
Founded by Royal Charter (King James VI), ratified by the Scottish Parliament 1672.

By 1700 the name was 'The Faculty of Physicians and Surgeons of Glasgow'.

In 1909 King Edward VII permitted the use of the adjective 'royal'.

Became 'The Royal College of Physicians and Surgeons of Glasgow' by Act of Parliament, 6 December 1962.

1667   Royal College of Physicians of Ireland
1st Royal Charter 8 August 1667 referred to '... Praesidentis et Sociorum Collegii Medicorum in Dublin'.

2nd Charter from William and Mary, 15 Dec. 1692, named it the 'King and Queen's College of Physicians'. Name changed in 1890 to 'Royal College of Physicians of Ireland'.

1681   Royal College of Physicians of Edinburgh
Founded 29 Nov. 1681 with this name by its 'Charter of Erection' (Charles II); confirmed by 'Charter of Ratification', 16 June 1685 (James II).

Name confirmed as 'Royal College of Physicians of Edinburgh' by Royal Warrant for Charter of Incorporation, 16 August 1861.

1687   Royall Colledge of Physitians in Kilkenny
Charter of Incorporation 10 Nov. 1687 (James II) – the college disappeared after the King was deposed at the end of 1688.

1784   Royal College of Surgeons in Ireland
1st Charter 11 Feb. 1784 named it thus in English.

1800   Royal College of Surgeons of England
1st Charter sealed 22 March 1800 naming it 'Royal College of Surgeons in London'. (It was the successor to the Company of Surgeons, founded 1745, and the latter date is sometimes given for the origin of the RCS.)

New Royal Charter 1843; name changed to 'Royal College of Surgeons of England'.

1926   Royal College of Psychiatrists
The Medico-Psychological Association (so named from 1865 – founded in 1841

as the Association of Medical Officers of Asylums and Hospitals for the Insane) became Royal M.-P.A. by Royal Charter.

Became Royal College of Psychiatrists by supplemental Charter 16 June 1971.

1928   Royal College of Nursing
College of Nursing Ltd established March 1916.
   Royal Charter 1928.
   Granted authority for the prefix 'Royal' 1939.

1929   Royal College of Obstetricians and Gynaecologists
Founded 1929 as British College of Obstetricians and Gynaecologists.
   Name Royal College of Obstetricians and Gynaecologists authorised 1938.
   Royal Charter granted in 1946.

1941   Royal College of Midwives
Founded 1881 with title 'Matrons' Aid Society or Trained Midwives Registration Society' 1881, changed by 1886 to Midwives Institute.
   Became College of Midwives 1941.
   Granted Royal Charter 1947.

1947   Faculty of Dental Surgery
Founded 1947 as a faculty of the RCS of England.

1952   Royal College of General Practitioners
Founded 23 October 1952 as the College of General Practitioners.
   Permitted to add 'Royal' to name, 6 December 1967.
   Became Royal College of General Practitioners by Royal Charter, 23 October 1972.

1953   Royal College of Radiologists
Founded as Faculty of Radiologists 1939.
   Royal Charter 27 May 1953 for the Faculty.
   Became Royal College of Radiologists by supplemental Charter 1975.

1970   Royal College of Pathologists
Founded June 1962 as the College of Pathologists.
   Charter of Royal College of Pathologists, February 1970.

1972   Faculty of Community Medicine
Founded as a joint faculty of the RCPs of Glasgow, Edinburgh and London.
   Name changed in 1989 to Faculty of Public Health Medicine.

1978   Faculty of Occupational Medicine
Founded as a faculty of the RCP of London.

1988   Royal College of Ophthalmologists
Faculty of Ophthalmologists became College of Ophthalmologists by Royal Charter 1988.
   Permitted to add 'Royal' to the name 1993.

1989   Faculty of Pharmaceutical Medicine
Founded as a joint faculty of the RCPs of Glasgow, Edinburgh and London.

1992   Royal College of Anaesthetists
Faculty of Anaesthetists (founded 1948) became College of Anaesthetists within RCS 1988.
   Became Royal College of Anaesthetists by Royal Charter 1992.

1993   Faculty of Accident and Emergency Medicine
Founded as a joint faculty of the RCP of London and the RCS of England.

1993   Faculty of Family Planning and Reproductive Health Care
Founded as a faculty of the Royal College of Obstetricians and Gynaecologists.

1996   Royal College of Paediatrics and Child Health
British Paediatric Association became RCPCH by Royal Charter July 1996.

The Journal of the Royal College of Physicians *of London is referred to as* JRCPL.

Adams, R.   Cases of the heart accompanied with pathological observations. *Dublin Hospital Reports*, 1827.

Aminoff, M.   *Brown-Séquard, a visionary of science.* New York: Raven Press, 1993.

Annotations: Turning Point.   *Lancet*, 25 May 1946.

Baillie, M.   *The morbid anatomy of some of the most important parts of the human body.* London: J. Johnson, 1793.

Baillie, M.   *A series of engravings, which are intended to illustrate accompanied with explanations, the morbid anatomy of some of the most important parts of the human body.* London: J. Johnson, 1799–[1802]; 2nd ed. London: G. & W. Nicol, 1812.

Ball, K.; Fletcher, C.   Correspondence between Dr Keith Ball and Dr Charles Fletcher.   ASH archive, Contemporary Medical Archives Centre (CMAC), Wellcome Library.

Barnes, John.   A few remarks on the natives of Van Diemen's Land: paper read at the Royal College of Physicians. [n.d.]. RCP MSS 3058/1–3.

Bateman, T.   *Delineations of cutaneous diseases …* London: Longman, 1817.

Bateman, T.   Delineations of cutaneous diseases. (RCP MS.158).

Bateman, T.   Watercolour drawings of skin diseases made for Thomas Bateman, 1792–1806. (RCP MS.159).

Bateman, T.   Watercolour drawings of skin diseases made for Thomas Bateman, 1797–1814. (RCP MSS 748/5–119).

Beck, R. T.   *The cutting edge: early history of the surgeons in London.* [London]: Lund Humphries, 1974. (Text of 1423 petition on pages 63–67).

Bedford, D. E.   On collecting a cardiological library. *JRCPL*, 1972.

Bennett, J. W.   John Morer's will: Thomas Linacre and Prior Sellyng's Greek teaching. *Studies in the Renaissance*, 1968.

Bennion, E.   *Antique medical instruments.* London: Sotheby Parke Bernet, 1979.

Berridge, V.   Science and policy: the case of post-war British smoking policy. In: Lock, S. P. *et al* (eds) *Ashes to ashes: the history of smoking and health.* Amsterdam: Rodopi, 1998.

Berry, D.; Mackenzie, C.   *Richard Bright, 1789–1859: physician in an age of revolution and reform.* London: Royal Society of Medicine Services, 1992.

Besterman, E. The Evan Bedford Library of Cardiology and its catalogue. *British Heart Journal*, 1978.

Bettany, G. T. Sir Henry Halford. In *Dictionary of National Biography*, vol.24 Stephen, L.; Lee, S. (eds). London: Smith, Elder, 1890.

Bettany, G. T. William Hunter. In *Dictionary of National Biography*, vol.28 Lee, S. (ed.). London: Smith, Elder, 1891.

Birken, W. J.   Dr. John King (1614–81) and Dr. Assuerus Regemorter (1615–50), brethren in the Dutch Church and in the Royal College of Physicians of London, with added references to other 'Dutch' congregants in the Royal College, Dr. Baldwin Hamey and Dr. George Ent. *Medical History*, 1976.

Birken, W. J. The Puritan connexions of Sir Edward Alston, President of the Royal College of Physicians 1655–66. *Medical History*, 1974.

Birken, W. J. The Royal College of Physicians of London and its support of the Parliamentary cause in the English Civil War. *Journal of British Studies*, 1983.

Birken, W. J. The social problem of the English physician in the early seventeenth century. *Medical History*, 1987.

Black, D. A. K.   Robert Platt.   In *Dictionary of National Biography 1971–1980* Blake, (Lord); Nicholls, C. S. (eds). Oxford: Oxford University Press, 1986.

Bloom, J. H.; James, R. R. *Medical practitioners in the diocese of London, licensed under the Act of 3 Henry VIII, c.11: and annotated list 1529–1725.* Cambridge: University Press, 1935. (Text of 1511 Act on p.1–2).

Booth, C. C.   Sir Samuel Garth F.R.S.: the Dispensary poet. *Notes and Records of the Royal Society*, 1986.

Booth, C. C. Smoking and the gold-headed cane. In: *Balancing act: essays to honour Stephen Lock.* London: Keynes Press, 1991.

Boswell, E. The library of the Royal College of Physicians in the Great Fire. *The Library*, 1929–30.

Bright, R.   *Reports of medical cases …* 2 vols in 3. London: Longman, 1827–31.

Bright, R.; Say, F. R. *et al.* Pathological drawings and watercolours, with case notes, 1822–39. RCP MSS 974/1–106.

British Library. Reference Division. *William Caxton: an exhibition to commemorate the quincentenary of the introduction of printing into England …* London: British Museum Publications, 1976.

British Library. Sloane manuscript 3914, fol.66v–67; 3915, fol.23–24v.

British Medical Association. *The British Medical Association's proposals for a general medical service for the nation.* London: BMA, 1930.

British Medical Journal 23 May 1896.

British Medical Association. Collective Investigation Committee. *The collective investigation record*; Sir G. M. Humphry, F. A. Mahomed (eds). 2 vols. London: BMA, 1883–4.

British Thoracic Association. Death from asthma in two regions of England. *British Medical Journal*, 1982.

Brooks, E. St J. *Sir Hans Sloane: the great collector and his circle.* London: Batchworth Press, 1954.

Browne, T. *The works of Sir Thomas Browne*; ed. G. Keynes. London, Faber & Faber, 1928.

Bull, G. M. An examination of the final examination in medicine. *Lancet*, 1956.

Burns, A. *Observations on some of the most frequent and important diseases of the heart* ... Edinburgh: T. Bryce, 1809; [facsimile reprint, with an introduction by D. W. Richards. New York: Hafner, 1964].

Bylebyl, J. J. (ed.). *William Harvey and his age: the professional and social context of the discovery of the circulation.* Baltimore: Johns Hopkins University Press, 1979.

Causey, G. Letter form Professor Gilbert Causey to L.M. Payne, Librarian, Royal College of Physicians of London, 26 April 1966. (RCP files).

Charleton, W. *The immortality of the human soul, demonstrated by the light of nature; in two dialogues.* London: H. Herringham, 1657.

Choulant, L. *History and bibliography of anatomic illustration*; trans. and ed. M. Frank. Chicago: University of Illinois Press, 1920.

Christie, Manson & Woods, London, 24–26 March 1914. Lot 83, salver on foot, 1661, fetched £244 0s 3d (135/- per oz.).

Clark, G. N. *A history of the Royal College of Physicians of London.* Vols 1–2. Oxford: Clarendon Press, 1964–6.

Clayton, M. *The collectors' dictionary of the silver and gold of Great Britain and North America.* 2nd ed. Woodbridge: Antique Collectors' Club, 1985.

Colombo, Realdo. *De re anatomica libri xv.* Venice: N. Bevilacquae, 1559.

Cook, H. J. Against common right and reason: the College of Physicians versus Dr. Thomas Bonham. *American Journal of Legal History*, 1985.

Cook, H. J. *The decline of the old medical regime in Stuart London.* Ithaca, NY: Cornell University Press, 1986.

Cook, H. J. *Trials of an ordinary doctor: Joannes Groenevelt in seventeenth-century London.* Baltimore: Johns Hopkins University Press, 1994.

Cooke, A. M. *A history of the Royal College of Physicians of London.* Vol.3. Oxford: Clarendon Press, 1972.

Cooke, A. M. Daniel Whistler F.R.C.P. *JRCPL*, April 1967.

Cope, Z. *The Royal College of Surgeons of England: a history.* London: Blond, 1959.

Cormany, J. R. Jean Simon Chaudron: silversmith, poet and American pioneer. *Silver Magazine*, July, August, 1992.

Corrigan, D. On permanent patency of the mouth of the aorta, or inadequacy of the aortic valves. *Edinburgh Medical Journal*, 1832.

Craig, W. S. *History of the Royal College of Physicians of Edinburgh.* Oxford: Blackwell Scientific, 1976.

Crainz, F. (ed.) *The life and works of Matthew Baillie ... (1761–1823).* [Rome]: Peliti Associati, [1996].

Creswell, C. H. *The Royal College of Surgeons of Edinburgh: historical notes from 1505 to 1905.* Edinburgh: Oliver and Boyd, 1926.

Cunningham, A. (ed.) *The English manuscripts of Francis Glisson (1): from Anatomia hepatis (The anatomy of the liver)*, 1654. Cambridge: Cambridge Wellcome Unit, 1993.

Cunningham, A. The historical context of Wharton's work on the glands. Wharton, T. *Adenographia* ... 1656; translated by Stephen Freer. Oxford: Clarendon Press, 1996.

Curtis, W. J. R. *Denys Lasdun: architecture, city, landscape.* London: Phaidon Press, 1994.

De Beer, G. R. *Sir Hans Sloane and the British Museum.* London: Oxford University Press, 1953.

Dobson, J.; Milnes Walker, R. *Barbers and barber-surgeons of London: a history of the Barbers' and Barber-Surgeons' Companies.* Oxford: Blackwell Scientific, 1979.

Eccles, S. D.; Dawson, Bertrand Edward, Viscount Dawson of Penn. In *Dictionary of National Biography 1941–50.* Wickham Legg, L. G.; Williams, E. T. (eds). London: Oxford University Press, 1959.

Edwards, G. *A natural history of uncommon birds* ... 4 vols. London: the Author, 1743–51.

Edwards, G. *Gleanings of natural history* ... 3 vols. London: the Author, 1758–64.

Elgood, C. L. *A medical history of Persia and the Eastern Caliphate* ... Cambridge: Cambridge University Press, 1951.

Elgood, C. L. *Safavid medical practice* ... London: Luzac, 1970.

Elgood, C. L. *Safavid surgery.* London: Pergamon Press, 1966.

English, M. P. *Victorian values: the life and times of Edwin Lankester M.D., F.R.S.* Bristol: Biopress, 1990.

Ent, G. Praelectiones anatomica habitae in aedib. Collegii Medicorum Lond. 13, 14, 15 Aprilis 1665. (RCP MS.130).

Evelyn, J. An account of divers schemes of arteries and veins, dissected from adult human bodies, and given to the repository of the Royal Society. *Philosophical Transactions*, 1702.

Evelyn, J. *Diary.* Ed. E. S. de Beer. Vols 2 & 3. Oxford: Clarendon Press, 1955.

Fine, L. G. Pathological specimens of the kidney examined. *Kidney International*, 1986.

Finn, R. *et al.* A much misunderstood caduceus and the case for an aesculapion. *Lancet*, 5 June 1999.

Fisher, R. B. *Edward Jenner 1749–1823.* London: Andre Deutsch, 1991.

Fleming, P. R. *et al.* Evolution of an examination: MRCP (UK). *BMJ*, 1974.

Fothergill, J. *Chain of friendship: selected letters of Dr John Fothergill* ... ; ed. B. C. Corner, C. C. Booth. Cambridge, MA: Belknap Press, 1971.

Fox, P. On the symbolism of the arms of John Caius and of the College caduceus. *The Caian*, 1 October 1985 to 30 September 1986.

Fracastoro, G. *Syphilis, sive morbus gallicus.* [Verona: n. pub., 1530].

Frank, R. *Harvey and the Oxford physiologists: a study in scientific ideas.* Berkeley: University of California Press, 1980.

Freeman, S. E. *Medals relating to medicine and allied sciences in the numismatic collection of Johns Hopkins University: a catalogue.* Baltimore: Evergreen House Foundation, 1964.

Freeman, S. E. The Browne prize medals. *Bulletin of the History of Medicine*, 1946.

Freind, J. *The history of physick, from the time of Galen to the sixteenth century* ... [2 vols]. London: J. Walthoe, 1725–6.

Fry, E. John Selden. In *Dictionary of National Biography*, vol.51 Lee, S. (ed.). London: Smith, Elder, 1897.

Funnell, P. *et al. Millais: portraits.* London: National Portrait Gallery, 1999.

Galen. *De sanitate tuenda libri sex*, T. Linacre interprete. Paris: G. Rubeum, 1517.

Garrod, A. E. Sir William Osler. In *Dictionary of National Biography 1912–21.* Davis, H. W. C.; Weaver, J. R. H. (eds). London: Oxford University Press, 1927.

Garth, S. *The Dispensary: a poem.* London: J. Nutt, 1699; reprinted in *Poems on affairs of state* ... Volume 6: 1697–1704; ed. F. H. Ellis. New Haven: Yale University Press, 1970.

General Medical Council. *British pharmacopoeia.* London: GMC, 1864; latest edition – London: Stationery Office, 2000.

Gere, C. The work of John Paul Cooper. *The Connoisseur*, November 1975.

Glisson, F. *Anatomia hepatis* ... London: O. Pullein, 1654.

Glisson, F. *et al. De rachitide, sive morbo puerili qui vulgo The rickets dicitur tractatus* ... London: L. Sadler & R. Beaumont, 1650; *A treatise of the rickets: being a disease common to children.* London: P. Cole, 1651.

Goldsmiths' Company. *Exhibition Catalogue: Explosion talent today, the 650th Birthday of the Worshipful Company of Goldsmiths 1327–1977*, Goldsmiths' Hall, London, 1977, no. 9: silver and silver-gilt centrepiece or rosebowl, 1961.

Goldsmiths' Company. *Exhibition catalogue: Leslie Durbin, fifty years of silversmithing.* Goldsmiths' Hall, London, July 1982: parcel-gilt basin, 1959.

Goldsmiths' Company. *Exhibition catalogue: Treasures of the 20th century*, 25 May–21 July 2000: champagne cups, 1911.

Goodall, C. A collection of College affairs. c.1680–1700. (RCP MS.2189).

Goodall, C. *The Royal College of Physicians founded and established by law.* London: W. Kettilby, 1684.

[Goodall, C.] *A short account of the institution and nature of the College of Physicians, London; publish'd by themselves.* London: [RCP], 1686.

Gooddy-McCausland collection of Brown-Séquard papers. (RCP MSS 975–1000).

Graunt, J. *Natural and political observations ... upon the bills of mortality* ... London: J. Martin, 1662.

Gregg, I. A young Englishman's observations of the Aboriginals during five years in Van Diemen's Land. *Tasmanian Ancestry*, June 2000.

Grimshaw, M. The three Gabriels. *Proceedings of the Society of Silver Collectors*, 1972–4.

Gull, W. W. *A collection of the published writings*; ed. T. D. Acland. 2 vols. London: New Sydenham Society, 1894–6.

Halford, H. *On the education and conduct of a physician.* London: J. Murray, 1834.

Halford, H. On the necessity of caution in the estimation of symptoms in the last stages of some diseases. *Medical Transactions published by the College of Physicians in London*, 1810.

Hall, M. *Synopsis of the diastaltic nervous system* ... London: J. Mallett, [1850].

Hart, C. John Clarke M.D. c.1583–1653. *St Bartholomew's Hospital Journal*, February 1951.

Harvey, W. *An anatomical disputation concerning the movement of the heart and blood in living creatures*; translated with an introduction and notes by G. Whitteridge. Oxford: Blackwell Scientific, 1976.

Harvey, W. *The anatomical lectures of William Harvey*; ed. & trans. G. Whitteridge. Edinburgh: Livingstone, 1964.

Harvey, W. *The circulation of the blood and other writings*; translated by K.J. Franklin; introduction by Andrew Wear. London: Dent, 1990.

Harvey, W. *De motu locali animalium 1627*; ed., trans. and introduced by G. Whitteridge. Cambridge: Cambridge University Press, 1959.

Harvey, W. *Exercitatio anatomica de motu cordis et sanguinis in animalibus.* Frankfurt: W. Fitzer, 1628.

Harvey, W. *Exercitationes de generatione animalium* … London: O. Pulleyn, 1651; Disputations touching the generation of animals; trans. with an introduction and notes by G. Whitteridge. Oxford: Blackwell Scientific, 1981.

Harvey, W. Trust deed, 21 June 1656. (RCP MS.1024/385).

Heberden, E. *William Heberden: physician of the age of reason.* London: Royal Society of Medicine Services, 1989.

Heberden, W., the elder. [*Antitheriaka*], *or an essay on mithridatium and theriaca.* Cambridge, 1745.

Heberden, W., the elder. A plan for the reception and publication of medical papers ... March 24, 1766. (Printed). (RCP MS.2537).

Heberden, W., the elder. *Commentaries on the history and cure of diseases.* London: T. Payne, 1802. Reprinted – New York: Hafner, 1962; Birmingham, AL: Classics of Medicine Library, 1982.

Heberden, W., the elder. *Commentarii de morbum historia et curatione.* London: T. Payne, 1802.

Heister, L. *A compendium of the practice of physic* … trans. from the Latin by E. Barker. London: J. Payne, 1757.

Hodgkin, T. Holograph letter to Thomas Nunneley, 2 August 1843. (RCP autograph letters collection).

Holinshed, R. *Holinshed's Chronicles of England, Scotland and Ireland.* – vol.4. London: J. Johnson, 1808. (Typed extract in Lumleian lectures file in RCP Library).

Honigsbaum, F. *Health, happiness, and security: the creation of the National Health Service.* London: Routledge, 1989.

Hope, J. *A treatise on diseases of the heart and great vessels* ... 3rd ed. London: Churchill, 1839.

House of Commons. Select Committee on Medical Education. *Report ... with minutes of evidence and appendix.* (Chairman: Henry Warburton). [London]: 13 August 1834.

Hughes, G. Contemporary British craftsmen: Gerald Benney. *The Connoisseur*, December 1963.

Hull, A.; Geyer-Kordesch, J. *The shaping of the medical profession: the history of the Royal College of Physicians and Surgeons of Glasgow, 1858–1999.* London: Hambledon Press, 1999.

Interdepartmental Committee on Social Insurance and Allied Services. *Social insurance and allied services: report*, by Sir William Beveridge. 2 vols. London: HMSO, 1942.

Jenner, E. *An inquiry into the causes and effects of the variolae vaccinae: a disease discovered in the western counties of England, particularly Gloucestershire, and known by the name of the cow pox.* London: for the Author, 1798.

Jones, M. *The art of the medal.* London: British Museum Publications, 1979.

Kark, R. M. Editorial: a prospect of Richard Bright on the centenary of his death, December 16, 1858. *American Journal of Medicine*, 1958.

Keynes, G. *The portraiture of William Harvey.* (Vicary Lecture, 1948). London: Royal College of Surgeons of England, 1949. Reprinted London: Keynes Press, 1985.

Keynes, G. *The life of William Harvey.* Oxford: Clarendon Press, 1966.

Lasdun, D. L. An architect's approach to architecture. *R.I.B.A. Journal*, 1965.

Leach, D.; Beckwith, J. The founders of dermatology: Robert Willan and Thomas Bateman. *JRCPL*, 1999.

Leach, D.; Beckwith, J. Dr John Mitchell Bruce's notes relating to the last illness and death of Benjamin Disraeli. *Journal of Medical Biography* (forthcoming).

Lee, G. E. *British silverware Monteith bowls.* Byfleet: Manor House Press, 1978.

Linacre, T. *De emendata structura latini sermonis.* London: R. Pynson, 1524.

Linacre, T. *Rudimenta grammatices.* London: R. Pynson, [1523?].

Locke, J. *An essay concerning humane understanding.* London: E. Mory, 1690.

Lovell R. R. H. *Churchill's doctor: a biography of Lord Moran.* London: Royal Society of Medicine Services, 1992.

McDonald, W. I. The College and the NHS. *JRCPL*, 1998.

McGrew, R. E. *Encyclopedia of medical history.* London: Macmillan, 1985.

Macmichael, W. *The gold-headed cane.* London: J. Murray, 1827.

Macmichael, W. *The gold-headed cane.* 2nd ed. London: J. Murray, 1828.

Macmichael, W. *The gold-headed cane: facsimile of the author's 1827 copy interleaved, with his own amendments and additions.* London: Royal College of Physicians, 1968.

Macmichael, W. *The gold-headed Cane.* [New edition]; ed. [with three additional chapters] by W. Munk. London: Longmans, Green, 1884.

Maddison, F. *et al* (eds). *Essays on the life and work of Thomas Linacre c.1460–1524* (Linacre studies). Oxford: Clarendon Press, 1977: editors' introduction, chapters by C. B. Schmitt, C. Webster, G. Barber, M. Hill.

Mason, A. S. *George Edwards: the Bedell and his birds.* London: Royal College of Physicians, 1992.

Mason, A. S. The arms of the College. *JRCPL*, 1992.

Maxwell, R. Royal College of Physicians, Regent's Park, London: architects Denys Lasdun and Partners [review]. *Architectural Review*, 1965.

Medical Transactions published by the College of Physicians in London. 6 vols. 1768–1810.

Merrett, C. *A collection of acts of Parliament, charters, trials at law and judges opinions concerning those grants to the Colledge of Physicians London* … [London: College of Physicians], 1660.

Middleton, B. C. *A history of English craft bookbinding technique.* 4th ed. New Castle, DE: Oak Knoll Press and London: The British Library, 1996.

Miles, A. *The Edinburgh School of Surgery before Lister.* London, A. & C. Black, 1918.

Millar, E. G. Psautier historié du XIIIe siècle exécuté pour l'abbaye de Wilton … In his *Les manuscrits à peintures des bibliothèques de Londres.* Paris, 1914–20.

Ministry of Health. Consultative Council on Medical and Allied Services. *Interim report on the future provision of medical and allied services.* (Chairman: Lord Dawson of Penn) (Cmd.693). London: HMSO, 1920.

Moore, N. Matthew Baillie. In *Dictionary of National Biography*, vol.2. Stephen, L. (ed.). London: Smith, Elder, 1885.

Moore, N. William Harvey. *Dictionary of National Biography*, vol.25. Stephen, L.; Lee, S. (eds). London: Smith, Elder, 1891.

Moran (Lord) *The anatomy of courage.* London: Constable, 1945; 2nd ed. London: Constable, 1966.

Moran, (Lord) [Editorial]: The hospitals and democracy. *St Mary's Hospital Gazette*, July 1910.

Moran, (Lord) Typed letter with typed signature, 24 August 1943, to Sir John (later Lord) Stopford FRCP. 3 pages. (RCP archives: NHS documents, box 7, file 3, no.74).

Moran, (Lord) *Winston Churchill: the struggle for survival, 1940–1965.* London: Constable, 1966.

Munk, W. *The life of Sir Henry Halford.* London: Longmans, Green, 1895.

Munk, W. *The Roll of the Royal College of Physicians of London.* 2nd ed. London: RCP, 1878; and its continuation as *Lives of the Fellows of the Royal College of Physicians of London [1826–97].* Vols 4–10. London: RCP, 1955–2000; continuing on the RCP website – www.rcplond.ac.uk/pubs/ munk_home.htm

Munk, W. Letter to the Registrar, Sir Henry Pitman, 2 April 1884. (RCP autograph letters collection)

Newman, C. E. The first library of the Royal College of Physicians. (FitzPatrick Lecture 1968). *JRCPL*, April 1969.

Newman, C. E. The history of the College library, 1879–99. *JRCPL*, January 1984.

Newman, C. E. New light on the Musaeum Harveianum. *JRCPL*, April 1978.

Nixon, H. M. *Five centuries of English bookbinding.* London: Scolar Press, 1978.

Norman, J. M. (ed.) *Morton's medical bibliography* … (Garrison and Morton). 5th ed. Aldershot: Scolar Press, 1991.

Nutton, V. Roman medicine, 250 BC to AD 200. In: Conrad, L. I. *et al. The Western medical tradition 800 BC to AD 1800.* Cambridge: Cambridge University Press, 1995.

Nutton, V. John Caius and the Linacre tradition. *Medical History*, 1979.

Nutton, V. *John Caius and the manuscripts of Galen.* [Cambridge]: Cambridge Philological Society, 1987.

Ord, W. M. A short account of the life and writings of Dr. Sibson. In: Sibson, F. *Collected works* ... London: Macmillan, 1881.

Osler, W. Letters to Horace Barlow. 20th cent. (RCP autograph letters collection).

Osler, W. *Bibliotheca Osleriana: a catalogue of books illustrating the history of medicine and science* ... Oxford: Clarendon Press, 1929.

Palmer, R. Some extracts of Dr. Baldwin Hamey's benefactions to the College of Physicians in London. Some extracts of Dr. Baldwin Hamey's public benefactions not relating to the College of Physicians in London. RCP legal documents, envelope 322.

Palmer, R. The life of the most eminent Dr. Baldwin Hamey. 1733. (RCP MS.337).

Parliament. Royal College of Physicians of London Act, 1960; 8 & 9 Eliz.2, Ch.xvii; Section 3.

Payne, J. F. Richard Bright. In *Dictionary of National Biography*. vol.6. Stephen, L. (ed.). London: Smith, Elder, 1886.

Payne, J. F. Thomas Linacre. In *Dictionary of National Biography*, vol.33. Lee, S. (ed.). London: Smith Elder, 1893.

Payne, J. F. William Heberden, the elder. *Dictionary of National Biography*, vol.25 Stephen, L., Lee, S. (eds). London: Smith, Elder, 1891.

Payne, L. M. From the Librarian's desk: [the College mace]. *College Commentary*, January 1973.

Payne, L M. Tabulae Harveianae: a 17th-century teaching aid. *British Medical Journal*, 2 July 1966.

Payne, L. M.; Newman, C. E. Dr Munk, Harveian Librarian: the first period. *JRCPL*, April 1977.

Payne, L. M.; Newman, C. E. History of the College library 9: Dr Munk as Harveian Librarian 2 (1862–70). *JRCPL*, January 1978.

Payne, L. M.; Newman, C. E. The history of the College library: George Edwards, Library Keeper. *JRCPL*, January 1973.

Payne, L. M.; Newman, C. E. The history of the College library 1688–1727. *JRCPL*, July 1971.

Payne, L. M.; Newman, C. E. The history of the College library 1760–92: in the time of George III. *JRCPL*, April 1974.

Payne, L. M.; Newman, C. E. The history of the College library: the Dorchester Library. *JRCPL*, April 1970.

Payne, L. M.; Newman, C. E. The history of the College library: the eighteen-seventies. *JRCPL*, July 1984.

Payne, L. M.; Newman, C. E. The history of the College library: the last thirty years in Warwick Lane. *JRCPL*, October 1974.

Payne, L. M.; Newman, C. E. The history of the College library: the new library in Pall Mall. *JRCPL*, January 1977.

Payne, L. M.; Wilson, L. G.; Hartley, H. William Croone, F.R.S. (1633–84). *Notes and Records of the Royal Society*, 1960.

Peachey, G. C. The two John Peacheys. seventeenth-century physicians: their lives and times. *Janus*, 1918.

Peacock, T. B. *On malformations of the human heart ...* 2nd ed. London: Churchill, 1866.

Pelling, M. Knowledge, common and acquired: the education of unlicensed practitioners in early modern London. In: Nutton, V.; Porter, R. (eds) *The history of medical education in Britain.* Amsterdam: Rodopi, 1995.

Pelling, M. Medical practice in early modern England: trade or profession. In: Prest, W. (ed.) *The professions in early modern England.* London: Croom Helm, 1987.

Pelling, M.; Webster, C. Medical practitioners. In: Webster, C. (ed.) *Health, medicine and mortality in the sixteenth century* Cambridge: Cambridge University Press, 1979.

Pierrepont, Henry, 1st Marquis of Dorchester. Last will and testament, dated 22 March 1679, proved 1 February 1680. (Photostat copy in RCP library, MS.2000/130).

Pinches, J. H. *Medals by John Pinches: a catalogue of works struck by the company from 1840 to 1969.* London: Heraldry Today, 1987.

Poor Law Commissioners. *Report ... on an enquiry into the sanitary condition of the labouring population of Great Britain* [by E. Chadwick]. London: HMSO, 1842; [reprint]; edited with an introduction by M. W. Flinn. Edinburgh: Edinburgh University Press, 1965.

Power, D'Arcy. Sir Richard Quain. In *Dictionary of National Biography*, [1st] supplement, vol.3. Lee, S. (ed.). London: Smith, Elder, 1901.

Primerose, J. *Exercitationes et animadversiones in librum G. Harveii de motu cordis et circulatione sanguinis.* London, 1630.

Robb-Smith, A. H. T. A history of the College's Nomenclature of diseases: its preparation. *JRCPL*, 1969.

Robb-Smith, A. H. T. A history of the College's Nomenclature of diseases: its reception. *JRCPL*, 1969.

Robb-Smith, A. H. T. The quatercentenary of the Lumleian Lecture. *JRCPL*, 1983.

Roberts, J.; Watson, A. *John Dee's library catalogue.* London: Bibliographical Society, 1990.

Roberts, R. H. The personnel and practice of medicine in Tudor and Stuart England. Part II: London. *Medical History*, 1964.

Royal College of Physicians of London. *Annals 1518 to date*: ie minutes of the general meetings of the Fellows and (to 1938) of the Censors' Board. The title of the early volumes varies according to the language used, but 'Annals' is generally accepted as the short and uniform title for the whole series. Quotations in this book from the Latin of volumes 1–5 are taken from the English translation made for the College in the early 1950s.

Royal College of Physicians of London. Cash book 1664–1726 (MS.2041).

Royal College of Physicians of London. *A catalogue of the legal and other documents in the archives of the Royal College of Physicians of London.* (Typescript) 1924.

Royal College of Physicians of London. *The charter, bye-laws and regulations ...* London: RCP, 1886.

Royal College of Physicians of London. *The charter & bye-laws ... and the Acts of Parliament especially relating thereto.* London: RCP, 1933.

Royal College of Physicians of London. *The charter & bye-laws ...* London: RCP, 1975.

Royal College of Physicians of London. *The charter & bye-laws ...* London: RCP, January 1995.

Royal College of Physicians of London. Committee to report on smoking and atmospheric pollution. Minutes of meetings. 1959 onward. RCP archive.

Royal College of Physicians of London. *The Evan Bedford Library of Cardiology: catalogue of books, pamphlets and journals.* London: RCP, 1977.

Royal College of Physicians of London. Exhibition catalogues (by Geoffrey Davenport): *Charles McMoran Wilson, Lord Moran, 1995; NHS50: the creation of the National Health Service, with special reference to the role of the RCP and its Fellows*, 1998.

Royal College of Physicians of London. Experience of multiple-choice-question examination for Part I of the M.R.C.P.: report of a study group. *Lancet*, 11 November 1967.

Royal College of Physicians of London. *Health or smoking?* London: Pitman, 1983.

Royal College of Physicians of London. The library account 1765 to 1838 (RCP MS.2086).

Royal College of Physicians of London. Medical Services Study Group. Death certification and epidemiological research; compiled by C. A. Clarke and A. G. W. Whitfield. *British Medical Journal*, 14 October 1978.

Royal College of Physicians of London. *Research Unit report 1977–84.* London: RCP, September 1984.

Royal College of Physicians. *Nicotine addiction in Britain.* London: RCP, 2000.

Royal College of Physicians of London. *Nomenclature of diseases.* London: RCP, 1869; 8th (and final) ed. London; HMSO, 1960.

Royal College of Physicians of London. *Portraits*; ed. G. E. W. Wolstenholme, D. Piper. London: Churchill, 1964.

Royal College of Physicians of London. *Portraits II*; ed. G. E. W. Wolstenholme, J. Kerslake. Amsterdam: Elsevier, 1977.

Royal College of Physicians of London. *Smoking and health.* London: Pitman Medical,1962.

Royal College of Physicians of London. *Smoking and health now.* London: Pitman Medical, 1971.

Royal College of Physicians of London. *Smoking and the young.* London: RCP, 1992.

Royal College of Physicians of London. *Smoking or health?.* London: Pitman Medical, 1977.

Royal College of Physicians of London. Statuta 1647. (MS.2012/58); [Statutes 1696]. (MS.2012/65); Statuta 1811: President's copy. (MS.2012/90).

Royal College of Physicians of London. *The statutes of the Colledge of Physicians London: worthy to be perused by all men ...* [with an English translation by John Badger]. [London], 1693.

Royal College of Physicians of London. Statutes 1555–63 (surviving copy of Caius' text). Bodleian Library MS. Ashmole 1826.

Royal Commission on Medical Education. *Report ...* (Chairman: Lord Todd). London: HMSO, 1968.

Royal Society of London. *Record of the Royal Society of London ...* 4th ed. London: Royal Society, 1940.

Schouten, J. *The rod and serpent of Asklepios: symbol of medicine.* Amsterdam: Elsevier, 1967.

Sharp, Lindsay. The Royal College of Physicians and Interregnum politics. *Medical History*, 1975.

Sheldon, Elizabeth. Conservation report on Edward Jenner by Sir Thomas Lawrence, May 1992. (In RCP Library and Information Service files).

Sibson, F. Pathological and clinical illustrations. RCP MSS 793/1–382.

Sibson, F. *Medical anatomy, or, illustrations of the relative position and movements of the internal organs.* London: J. Churchill, 1869.

Sibson, F. On the changes induced in the situation and structure of the internal organs, under varying circumstances of health and disease; and on the nature and external indications of these changes. *Transactions of the Provincial Medical and Surgical Association*, 1844. Also in *Collected works ...* London: Macmillan, 1881.

Sloane, H. *A voyage to the islands of Madera, Barbados, Nieves, S. Christophers and Jamaica, with a natural history ... of the last of those islands.* 2 vols. London: the Author, 1707–25.

Smerdon, G. T. Daniel Whistler and the English disease: a translation [from Latin to English of Whistler's 1645 Leyden thesis *De morbo puerili anglorum*] and a biographical note. *Journal of the History of Medicine and Allied Sciences*, 1959.

Snowman, K. Gerald Benney – silversmith. *The Connoisseur*, May 1973.

Steinberg, S. H. *Five hundred years of printing.* 3rd ed. Harmondsworth: Penguin Books, 1974.

Stevenson, L. G. The siege of Warwick Lane, together with a brief history of the Society of Collegiate Physicians, 1767–98. *Bulletin of the History of Medicine* 1952.

Storer, H. R. *Medicina in nummis: a descriptive list of the coins, medals [and] jetons relating to medicine, surgery and allied sciences*; ed. M. Storer. Boston, MA: Wright and Potter, 1931.

Symons, J. Symons collection: list as displayed (draft catalogue), November 1997.

Symons, J. The Symons collection: origins and contents. *JRCPL*, 1997.

Thompson, E. *Corpus silver*; ed. C. Ellory *et al.* Oxford, 1999.

Thompson, E. The Swiney Prize. *Apollo Magazine*, January 1995.

Tritton, A. S. Catalogue of the oriental manuscripts in the library of the Royal

College of Physicians. *Journal of the Royal Asiatic Society*, October 1951.

Urdang, G. *Pharmacopoeia Londinensis of 1618*: reproduced in facsimile, with a historical introduction by George Urdang. Madison: State Historical Society of Wisconsin, 1944.

Vander, R. Some Sheffield silversmiths. *Proceedings of the Society of Silver Collectors.*

Venn, J. *Biographical history of Gonville and Caius College.* Vol.3. Cambridge: University Press, 1901.

Victoria & Albert Museum. *Second stock book, 1914–38* (with entries from 1909). 15 November 1911.

Waddington, I. The struggle to reform the Royal College of Physicians, 1767–71: a sociological analysis. *Medical History*, 1973.

Wear, A. Medicine in early modern Europe, 1500–1700. In: Conrad, L. I. [*et al*]. *The Western medical tradition 800 BC to AD 1800.* Cambridge: Cambridge University Press, 1995.

Wear, A. William Harvey and the way of the anatomists. *History of Science*, 1983.

Webster, C. Tobacco smoking addiction: a challenge to the National Health Service. *British Journal of Addiction*, 1984.

Webster, C. The College of Physicians: 'Solomon's House' in Commonwealth England. *Bulletin of the History of Medicine*, 1967.

Wharton, T. *Adenographia …* London: [the Author], 1656; [facsimile reprint with an English translation by Stephen Freer]. Oxford: Clarendon Press, 1996.

Whistler, D. *Disputatio medica inauguralis de morbo puerili anglorum quem patrio idiomate indigeae vocant The rickets.* Leyden: W. C. Boxius, 1645.

Whitfield, A. G. W. *The Royal College of Physicians: the first thirty-seven Registrars of the College.* [Sutton Coldfield: the Author, 1981].

Whitteridge, G. Some Italian precursors of the Royal College of Physicians. *JRCPL*, 1977.

Whitteridge, G. *William Harvey and the circulation of the blood.* London: Macdonald, 1971.

Willan, R. *On cutaneous diseases.* London: J. Johnson, 1808.

Witt, R. G. The humanist movement. In: Brady, T. A. *et al* (eds). *Handbook of European history 1400–1600.* Leyden: Brill, 1994–5.

WORKS OF ART:

THOSE ACQUIRED SINCE 1977,

AND EARLIER ACQUISITIONS NOT NOTED IN THE
1964 AND 1977 PUBLISHED CATALOGUES

Dimensions are given in the order height x width, to the nearest quarter-inch or half-centimetre.

Details listed in the following order: Subject, Artist and date, Medium and Dimensions, Provenance.

Portraits

BARLOW, Sir Thomas (1845–1945) Bt KCVO MD FRCP FRS : PRCP 1910–15; Catherine Dodgson, 1936; chalk on paper; bequest of Miss H.A.D. Barlow 1976.

BLACK, Sir Douglas Andrew Kilgour MD FRCP FFOM (1913–) : PRCP 1977–83; Richard Foster, 1983; oils on canvas, 35⁄ x 27⁄ inches, 89 x 69 cm.; commissioned by the RCP.

BROADBENT, Sir William Henry MD FRCP FRS (1835–1907); artist unknown; watercolour, 19⁄ x 16fl inches, 49 x 43 cm.; gift from Dr R. K. Mallya FRCP 1997.

CLARKE, Sir Cyril Astley KBE MD FRCP FFOM FRS (1907–2000) : PRCP 1972–7; Ruskin Spear, 1977; oils on canvas, 29fi x 24fl inches, 75 x 62.5 cm.; commissioned by the RCP.

COMPSTON, Nigel Dean CBE MA MD FRCP (1918–86) : Treasurer RCP 1970–85; Howard Morgan, 1985; oils on canvas, 24fi x 30fi inches, 62 x 77.5 cm.; commissioned by the RCP.

CONOLLY, John MD FRCP (1794–1866); copy by Red Bronze Studio of marble bust by Giovanni Maria Benzoni 1866, 1987; bronze cast, 21fi x 20 x 14 inches, 54.5 x 51 x 35.5 cm.; indefinite loan, 1996, from the Royal College of Psychiatrists, in exchange for the marble bust by Benzoni, originally deposited in the RCP by the RCPsych's predecessor body, the Royal Medico–Psychological Association, in 1867.

DALE Sir Henry Hallett OM GBE MA MD FRS (1875–1968) : PRS 1940–5; Nobel Prize 1936; Augustus John, 1955; chalk on paper; 18⁄ x 12fi inches, 46.5 x 31.5 cm.; bequest of F. H. K. Green FRCP 1977.

GULL, Sir William Withey MD FRCP FRS (1816–90); John Brooke Nash, 1937; paint-

ed wooden relief plaque of head; gift of the artist's son-in-law Mr H. Hinns, Mold, Clwyd, September 1985.

HEAD, Sir Henry MA MD FRCP FRS (1861–1940); Sir William Rothenstein, 1925; charcoal drawing 9 x 6fl inches, 22.5 x 17.5 cm.; gift from Dr Patrick Kidd FRCPath, September 1987.

HILL, Sir Austin Bradford CBE PhD HonFRCP FRS (1897–1991); Neil French, 1990; head in biscuit-fired clay, 11 x 9 x 8fi inches, 28 x 23 x 21.5 cm.; gift from the *British Medical Journal* 1991, who commissioned it for their 150th anniversary in 1990.

HOFFENBERG, Sir Raymond KBE MD FFOM (1923–) PRCP 1983–9; Dame Elisabeth Frink, 1990; bronze head, 12fl x 7⁄ x 9⁄ inches, 32.5 x 18.5 x 23.5 cm.; commissioned by the RCP.

INGRAM, John Thornton MD FRCP (1899–1972); Frank Eastman, 1959; oils on canvas, 49fi x 39fi inches, 126 x 100.5 cm.; gift from his widow Dame Kathleen Raven (1910–99), 1976.

LATHAM, John MD (1761–1843) : PRCP 1813–20; John Jackson, 1816; oils on canvas, 48fl x 39 inches, 124 x 99 cm.; indefinite loan from 23 August 1995 by Mr Christopher V. M. Latham, Leatherhead, Surrey.

LINACRE, Thomas MD (1460?–1524) : PRCP 1518–24; Henry Weekes, 1876; bust truncated from full-length statue; now 22 x 30⁄ x 15⁄ inches, 56 x 77 x 39cm.; statue commissioned by RCP, formerly in niche on facade of RCP building, Pall Mall East from 1876 to 1964 – bought back from Mr Albert Linacre.

McNEE, Sir John William MD DSc FRCP FRPSGlas FRSE(1887–1984); Sir James Gunn, date unknown; oils on board, 18 x 14 inches, 45.8 x 35.5 cm.; bequeathed to the RCP by the sitter.

PAPPWORTH, Maurice Henry (1910–94) MD FRCP; Mary Rose Bliss FRCP, 17 July 1994; crayon on paper, 14fi x 11 inches, 37 x 28 cm.; indefinite loan by the artist, September 1997.

PHEAR, Arthur George CB MD FRCP (1867–1959); Muriel Jackson: 'Dr Phear at the clavichord'; tempera on board, 22fi x 30fi inches, 57 x 77.5 cm.; bequest from Alice Margaret Craig Macpherson MD FRCP (1900–93).

POWELL, Henry (d. 1855) MD Edin. MRCS LSA; oils on canvas, J. Rawlings; gift from his 3 great-granddaughters: Mrs Joan Atkins, Marble Hall, Witnesham, Ipswich; Mrs A. R. Nilson, Pinner, Middlesex; and Dr Diana Griffith MB; received 30 May 1989.

PYKE, David Alan CBE MD FRCP (1921–2001): Registrar RCP 1975–92; Sue Ryder, 1993; oils on canvas, 29fi x 35fi inches, 75 x 90 cm.; commissioned by RCP.

SMYTH, James Carmichael FRCP FRS (1741–1821); artist unknown, *c*.1803; oils on canvas, 30 x 25 inches, 76 x 63.5 cm.; purchased from the family with a gift from Dr A.W. Frankland FRCP, 1999.

SQUIRE, William MD FRCP (1825–99); artist unknown, *c*.1846; pastel, oval 14 x 10 inches, 35.5 x 25.5 cm.; bust to right; bequest 1994.

TURNBERG, Sir Leslie Arnold MD (1934–) : PRCP 1992–7; Anthony Oakshett, 1997; oils on canvas, 35fi x 40fi inches, 90.5 x 103 cm.; commissioned by RCP.

TURNER-WARWICK, Dame Margaret Elizabeth Harvey DBE DM PhD FFOM (1924–) : PRCP 1989–92; David Poole, 1992; oils on canvas, 35⁄ x 27⁄ inches, 89.5 x 69 cm.; TQL seated; commissioned by RCP.

COMITIA 1968; Raymond Piper, 1968; oils on canvas, 39fi x 54fi inches, 100 x 138.5 cm.; commissioned by RCP; composite scene painted at several quarterly meetings of Comitia in the Dorchester Library.

Other Subjects

'AMARYLLIS AND HELLEBORE'; Norman Henry Ashton FRCP, 1997(?); oils on board, 19 x 16 inches, 48 x 41cm.; gift of the artist; No.9 (Glisson) (from 1997 Art exhibition).

'GIFFORD, LITTLE VENICE SOUTH'; Jeremy King, 1986; lithograph no.71 of 250; 16 x 24 inches, 40.5 x 61cm.; published CCA Galleries 1987; no.9 or 10.

'JON'; Marion Beatrice Ballinger MRCP 1997; acrylic on paper, 15⁄ x 11fi inches, 39.5 x 29.5 cm; signed at bottom right 'Marion Ballinger / 1997'; gift of the artist.

'PORTRAIT OF A GIRL'; Christopher W. Longmuir, 1997; chalk on paper, 18 x 11fi inches, 45.5 x 29.5 cm.; gift of the artist.

'PRIDE OF THE THAMES, LITTLE VENICE NORTH'; Jeremy King, 1986; lithograph, no.71 of 250; 16 x 24 inches, 40.5 x 61 cm.; published CCA Galleries 1987; gift of the artist.

'PROMETHEUS'; Ceri Richards, 1970; pen and watercolour on paper, 18 x 26fl inches, 45.7 x 68 cm.; given by Mrs Anna Harman in memory of Dr John Bishop Harman FRCP (1907–94), 1995.

PULKSTYE COTTAGE, Holtye Common, Cowden, Kent; Diana Mary Compston 1986; oils on canvas; gift of the artist.

RCP St Andrews Place, viewed from Regent's Park; John Plaistowe Horder FRCP FRCGP, 1994; watercolour on paper; 14fi x 21fi inches, 36.5 x 54.5 cm.; gift of the artist.

ST ANDREWS PLACE, viewed from RCP, no.11; John Plaistowe Horder FRCP FRCGP, 1994; watercolour on paper; 14fi x 21fi inches, 36.5 x 54.5 cm.; gift of the artist.

STILL LIFE; Marion Beatrice Ballinger MRCP, 1997; watercolour on paper, 21 x 14fl inches, 53.5 x 37.5 cm.; gift of the artist.

TRAFALGAR SQUARE seen from the old RCP building, Pall Mall East; Felix Kelly, 1964; oils on hardboard, 22 x 28 inches, 56 x 71 cm.; commissioned by the College.

VIEW OF NEFYN BAY FROM THE GOLF COURSE; Ramesh Kamalaksha Mallya FRCP; watercolour, 7/ x 10/ inches, 18.5 x 26 cm.; gift of the artist.

A VIEW OF NEFYN BAY ON A QUIET DAY; Ramesh Kamalaksha Mallya FRCP; watercolour, 6fl x 9fl inches, 17.5 x 24.5 cm.; gift of the artist.

A VIEW OF PORTHDILLAEN; Ramesh Kamalaksha Mallya FRCP; watercolour, 7/ x 10/ inches, 18.5 x 26 cm.; gift of the artist.

Portraits Removed from the College Since Publication of the 1977 Catalogue

CONOLLY, John MD FRCP (1794–1866); Giovanni Maria Benzoni, 1866; marble bust (Portraits [catalogue I], pages 138–9) loaned indefinitely to the Royal College of Psychiatrists in exchange for the bronze copy made for them in 1987 (see also acquisitions above); transferred on 9 October 1996.

DOWLING Geoffrey Barrow MD FRCP (1891–1976); Patrick Phillips (date unknown); oils on canvas; gift from Dowling family to British Association of Dermatologists 1977; transferred to the BAD, 19 Fitzroy Square, London, 17 January 1997.

GRAY, Sir Archibald Montague Henry KCVO CBE TD MD FRCS FRCP (1880–1967); Rodrigo Moynihan, 1956; oils on canvas. (Portraits catalogue II, pages 122–3); transferred to the British Association of Dermatologists, 19 Fitzroy Square, London, 17 January 1997.

HARVEY, Sir Eliab (1635–1698/9); artist unknown, 1675; oils on canvas. (Portraits catalogue II, pages 128–9); returned to the Harveian Society of London, 6 December 1993.

HARVEY, Lady Dorothy (1638–1725/6); artist unknown, 1675; oils on canvas. (Portraits catalogue II, pages 128, 130–1); returned to the Harveian Society of London, 6 December 1993.

ROOK, Arthur James MA MD FRCP (1915–91); Patrick Phillips, 1974; oils on canvas; gift from sitter's son, John Rook, to British Association of Dermatologists, November 1993; transferred to the BAD, 19 Fitzroy Square, London, 17 January 1997.

ROSENHEIM, Max Leonard, baron KBE MD FRCP FRS (1908–72): PRCP 1966–72; Rhoda Pepys, 1966; oils or acrylic on canvas. (Portraits catalogue II, pages 184–5); returned to the artist, 1993.

ROSENHEIM, Max Leonard, baron KBE MD FRCP FRS (1908–72): PRCP 1966–72; Rhoda Pepys (date unknown); brown chalk on buff paper. (Portraits catalogue II, p.184); returned to the artist, 1993.

WHITMORE, Anne (Lady) (d.1775); Edward Penny, 1757; oils on canvas. (Portraits catalogue II, pages 192–3); returned to the Harveian Society of London, 6 December 1993.

WILSON, Sir William James Erasmus FRCS FRS (1809–84); Stephen Pearce, c.1872; oils on canvas. (Portraits catalogue II, pages 194–5); transferred to the British Association of Dermatologists, 19 Fitzroy Square, London, 17 January 1997.

LIST OF SUBSCRIBERS

Bernard Adams FRCP FRCPsych
P. I. Adnitt MD FRCP FFPM
Professor Sir George Alberti KB BM PRCP
Dr Robert Allan MD PhD FRCP
B. Roger Allen FRCP
Dr T. A. S. Amos MRCP(UK)
R. H. Andrews MD FRCP
Dr John Marshall Annear MB BS FRCPEdin FRCPsych DPM DCH DTM&H DObstRCOG
Barbara M. Ansell CBE
P. G. Arblaster MD FRCP
Bryan Ashworth MD
Dr Prasert Assantachai MD(Hons) FRCP
Dr I. Aston MRCP(UK) FFOM
Professor Jon G Ayres MD FRCP
Anthony Bacon MD FRCP
Alan Bailey
Dr Mary J. Baldwin
Dr Andrew Bamji FRCP
Dr A. Banister MD FRCP
Dr R. A. Banks MD FRCP
Dr J. H. Baron DM FRCP FRCS
Dr R. Basu Roy FRCP FRCPEdin FRCS
Dr A. J. Batchelor CBE FRCP
Dr J. M. Bateman FRCP
Dr Anthony Batty Shaw FRCP
Rear Adm. G. J. A. Bayliss AM MRCP(UK)
Sir Richard Bayliss
Dr A. G. Bearn MD FRCP FACP
Professor D. G. Beevers MD FRCP
Dr John Bell FRCP
Dr Kathryn R. Bell MRCP(UK) FRCA
Christopher M. Bellamy FRCP
Dr John Bennett MD FRCP
Peter N. Bennett MD FRCP
Professor Robert Bennett MD FRCP
Dr S. J. Bentley FRCP
Professor Roger J. Berry FRCP FRCR FFOM
Dr Thomas Bewley CBE MD FRCP FRCPI FRCPsych
Dr H. L. Bhakri FRCP
Monica Bhushan BSc(Hons) MB ChB MRCP(UK)
David J. Bihari FRCP FRACP
Diana Bilton BSc MD FRCP
Dr James S. Bingham TD FRCP FRCOG
Dr George Bird FRCP
Professor H. A. Bird MD FRCP
Sir Douglas Black FRCP
Dr J. A. Black MD FRCP
Christopher R. Blagg MD FRCP
Professor A. J. M. Boulton MD FRCP
Professor Drummond H. Bowden
Dr I. M. Bowles FRCP
Professor John Bradley MD FRCP
Dr S. G. Brear FRCP
Dr J. L. Brennan MD MRCP FRCPath
Professor John Brocklehurst
Dr K. G. E. Brown MB MD FRCP
Professor M. M. Brown MD FRCP
Dr Felix Bruckner MB FRCP
Dr J. M. H. Buckler DM DSc FRCP
David Burman BSc MD FRCP

Mrs Pam Burn MA FIPD
Dr James A. Burton OStJ MB FRCP
Dr Andrew Bush MD FRCP
Dr C. M. Byatt MB FRCP
Dr J. P. H. Byrne FRCP FRCPI
Dr Michael E. Callender FRCP
Professor J. S. Cameron MD FRCP
Dr Ian A. Campbell BSc MD FRCP
Dr S. Campbell-Smith MB BS(Lond) FRCP
Catherine Carey FRCP
Dr M. Carpenter BSc MB ChB MRCP(UK)
Dr Jennifer Carroll
S. George Carruthers MD FRCP
Dr Michael J. D. Cassidy
Dr William Cattell MD FRCP FRCPEdin
Suphachai Chaithiraphan MD FRCP
Andrew L. Chan MB ChB MRCP(UK) FCCP FACP
Dr D. T. Chard MRCP(UK)
D. J. Charley OBE MD FRCP
Dr Ian Duncan Chisholm MA MB BS FRCP FRCPsych DPM
Dr G. H. Choa CBE MD FRCP
Dr Donald E Christian FRCP
Dr R. Chynoweth FRCP FRCPsych FRANZCP
Professor A. W. Clare MD FRCP
Arthur G. B. Clark MA FRCP
Dr C. J. M. Clark MD FRCP
Dr A. K. Clarke FRCP
Dr Angus J. Clarke
Dr B. Clarke BSc MB ChB MD FRCP FESC FACC
Dr G. P. Clein MD FRCP
Dr V. J. Clubb MB ChB MRCP
Dr P. M. Coats
Dr John R. Cockcroft FRCP
Professor Clive S. Cockram
Professor R. D. Cohen
Dr W. J. Coker FRCP
Mr Clive Constable
Dr Rosemary Cooper MA MB BChir FRCP
Professor J. R. M. Copeland MD FRCP FRCPsych
Dr Peter Corry FRCP
Dr J. E. Cosnett MD FRCP
J. A. Cotterill BSc MD FRCP
M. O. Coupe MD FRCP
Dr R. J. Courtenay-Evans FRCP
Dr George Cowan FRCP
R. E. Cowan MD FRCP
Alan W. Craft
Dr S. Michael Crawford MD FRCP FRCPEdin
Dr J. E. Creamer BSc FRCP
Professor Peter Crome MD PhD FRCP FFPM
Professor Emeritus Gareth Crompton HonMD(Wales) FRCP FFPHM
Dr R. F. P. Cronin MD FRCP
Leon Cudkowicz MD FRCP
Dr Derek R. Cullen MD FRCP
Dr D. Daley FRCP
Dr A. K. Dasgupta
Dr C. Davidson FRCP FESC
Derek Davies MA MB BChir(Cantab) FRCP
Dr Paget Davies MD FRCP

Dr Anthony G. Davison FRCP
Dr John M. Dawson MA MB FRCP FRCR
Miss Jane Gifford Denny
H. A. Dewar MD FRCP
Dr A. Graeme Dewhurst MA FRCP
Professor M. J. Dillon FRCP FRCPCH
Dr Anthony Dodi
Sir Richard Doll
Dr David Donaldson MB ChB FRCP
 FRCPath
Dr A. E. Dormer MD FRCP
Dr P. Dorrington Ward FRCP
Dr P. F. Down FRCP DHMSA
Lewis M. Drusin FRCP
Dr Tony Ducker TD FRCP FRCPCH
Dr P. R. Duncan MD FRCP
Dr J. M. Dunlop FRCP FFPHM FRPSL
Dr E. Caroline Dunn MB FRCP
Professor P. M. Dunn MA MD FRCP
 FRCOG FRCPCH
Dr T. Leslie Dunn FRCP FRCPsych
Dr M. G. S. Dunnill MD MRCP(UK)
Dr M. S. Dunnill MD FRCP FRCPath
Julian David Eason BSc MB BS MHSc DCH
 MRCP(UK) FRCPC FRCPCH
Philip Edmondson MD(Cantab) MRCP
Professor J. H. Edwards FRCP FRS
Frank Ellis OBE MA MSc MD DSc
 HonFRCP FRCR
Professor Roger Ellul-Micallef MD(Malta)
 PhD(Edin) FRCP FRCPEdin
Professor Alan Emery MD FRCP FRCPEdin
 FRSE
Dr Ellen S. Emslie FRCP
Donald Emslie-Smith MD FRCP
Dr B. A. Enoch FRCP
Emeritus Professor David A. Price Evans
 MD DSc PhD FRCP
Dr R. G. Evans FRCP
Professor M. J. G. Farthing MD FRCP
Dr G. C. Ferguson FRCP FRCPEdin
Professor Leon G. Fine FRCP FACP
 FRCPGlasg FMedSci
Dr P. Fletcher FRCP
R. F. Fletcher MD FRCP
Dr Jane Flint BSc MD FRCP
Dr Fong Ping Ching MB BS FRCPEdin
Dr Ian Forgacs MD FRCP
Dr Paul A. Fox MA MRCP
Dr Jeffrey S. Freeman FRCP
Sir Peter Froggatt FRCP
Dr W. J. Fysh FRCP FRCPCH
Dr M. J. Galloway BSc MBA MD FRCP
 FRCPath
Oliver P. Galpin FRCP
D. Gardner-Medwin MD FRCP
Christopher Gardner-Thorpe MD FRCP
Dr & Mrs J. A. Geffen
Dr Christine Gent BSc FRCP
Professor E. Paul Getaz MD MFA FRCP
 FRCPEdin FRCA(Canada) FACP
Dr David O. Gibbons FRCP
Professor G. J. Gibson BSc MD FRCP
Terence Gibson MD FRCP
Professor Ian T. Gilmore MD FRCP
Dr John Glasspool BM FRCP AIL
Dr Michael Glynn MA MD FRCP

Dr W. P. Goddard MA MRCP(UK) DM
Michael J. Goggin FRCP
Professor John M. Goldman DM FRCP
 FRCPath
N. S. Gordon
Dr Barry James Gray MD FRCP
Dr David Gray DM MPH FRCP
Emeritus Professor T. Cecil Gray CBE
 KCSG MD FRCP FRCS FRCA HonFFARCS
 HonFRANZCA
Major Ian Greaves RAMC
Professor Malcolm Green DM FRCP
Dr Charles Greenfield FRCP FRACP
Dr J. W. Gregory MB ChB MD FRCP
Professor George E. Griffin FRCP FRCPath
 FMedSci
Professor John P. Griffin FRCP FRCPath
 FFPM
T. A. Grimson MD FRCP
Dr Rajnish K. Gupta PhD FRCP
Dr Charles Gutteridge FRCP FRCPath
Professor David R. Hadden
Dr Michael Haggie OBE MC
Professor M. R. P. Hall FRCP
Dr Molly Hall
Professor H. L. Halliday MD FRCP
Jeremy Hallpike MD FRCP FRACP
Dr M. Hamilton OBE MD FRCP
Dr M. A. Hanid MD FRCP
Dr Owen Hanmer FRCP
Professor G. F. A. Harding DSc HonMRCP
C. A. Hardisty MD FRCP
Dr J. F. Hare FRCP
Dr M. Harington FRCP
Dr P. G. Harries MD FRCP FFOM
Professor J. M. Harrington CBE
Dr F. Dudley Hart
George Hart DM FRCP
Ian Haslock MD FRCP
John Hawkins
James C. Haworth MD FRCP
Sir David Hay CBE
Heberden Library, British Society for
 Rheumatology
Dr T. J. Hendra MD FRCP
Dr Neill C. Hepburn MD FRCP
Professor John Hickie AO FRCP FRACP
Arthur Hollman
J. M. Holt MA MD FRCP
Dr Richard I. G. Holt PhD MRCP(UK)
Dr N. P. Hudd MA FRCP
Dr P. Hudgson FRCP
W. A. Hudson FRCP
Professor J. M. B. Hughes DM FRCP
Dr P. J. Hughes RD MD FRCP
Professor R. A. C. Hughes MD FRCP
 FMedSci
Dr E. K. Hunter MB BCh BAO FRCP
Dr R. Michael Hutchinson MA BSc FRCP
Dr C. R. Hutchison
Dr R. D. Hyde MD FRCP
Charles Ilsley FRCP
D. H. Isaac MD FRCP
Professor Ian Isherwood MD FRCP FRCR
Sir Barry Jackson FRCS FRCP
Professor Malcolm IV Jayson
Dr T. A. Jeffers FRCPEdin

Dr Ewart Jepson MD FRCP
A. M. Johnson MD FRCP
Dr H. W. Jones FRCP
Dr J. Henry Jones MD FRCP
Professor J. Vann Jones FRCP
Dr Lydia Jones FRCP FRCPath
Professor W. Jones Williams MD FRCP
 FRCPath
Dr Michael Joy MD FRCP FACC FESC
 FRAeS
Dr A. C. Kaeser
Dr F. J. Kamlow MRCP(UK)
Dr Stephen Kane BM FRCP
Dr Yusuk Sidik Karim FRCP
John Kemm MD FRCP FFPHM
Dr Michael Kesseler FRCP
David Kindley FRCP
Professor Brian Kirby OBE FRCP
Haresh Kirpalani MSc FRCP FRCP(C)
Dr Paul Kist FRCP
Saulo Klahr MD FRCP
Dr Anthony H. Knight FRCP
Dr R. S. Kocen FRCP
Dr H. Kopelman FRCP
A. J. Larner
Professor Tak H. Lee MD ScD FRCP
 FRCPath
Dr Kevin Lee See MD BS FRCPEdin FRACP
Pierre J. Lefebvre MD PhD FRCP MAE
Dr D. Neil Leitch BSc(Hons) MB
 ChB(Hons) MRCP(UK) FRCP Dip Gpid
Dr V. M. Leveaux MD(Lond) FRCP
Dr Barry Lewis FRCP FRCPCH
David Lewis FRCP
Dr Kenneth C. L. Lim FRCP FRCPEdin
Professor Brian Livesley MD FRCP
Bernard Lloyd HonFRCP
Stephen Lock CBE MD
C. John L. Logan FRCP FRCGP
Professor R. Logan MD FRCP
Professor Ray Lowenthal
Dr John Ma FRCP
Dr C. Joan McAlpine FRCP
Dr W. O. McCormick FRCP
Dr Geoffrey Lance McDonald FRCP FRACP
Professor Ian McDonald FRCP FRCOpth
 FRACP
Dr Ross McHardy FRCP FRCPEdin
Professor Iain MacIntyre FRCP FRS
Dr C. G. McKerron MB FRCP
Surgeon Commodore Grant McMillan Royal
 Navy
Dr Andrew McNair
Dr Iain McQueen FRCP
Professor I. A. Magnus MA MD FRCP
Dr D. J. Mahad MRCP
Dr Robert Mahler FRCP FRCP(Edin)
Dr M. P. Mahoney FRCP
Dr Chris Marguerie MB BS FRCP
Marketing and Facilities Department, Royal
 College of Physicians
Philip Markman MD FRCP
Dr John Martin FRCP FRCPCH
Dr Vanessa Martlew FRCP FRCPath
Dr Hugh M. Mather MD FRCP
Dr M. B. Matthews MD FRCP
Professor G. E. Mawer

163

Dr R. J. Mawer
Dr R. L. Maynard CBE MRCP
Dr T. Meyer
Dr S. J. Middleton MD FRCP
Dr Christos Miltiades MD MRCP(UK) FESC
J. M. H. Moll DM PhD FRCP
Dr N. W. Morrell MD MRCP
Dr John S. Morris MD FRCP
Dr Pat Mortimer FRCP FRCPCH
Caroline Moss-Gibbons BLib PGCE
Dr E. S. Mucklow FRCP FRCPCH
Dr Lilian E. Murchison FRCP
Richard J. A. Murrin BSc MB ChB(Leic)
    MRCP(UK)
Dr M. P. Napier MB BS MRCP
G. Neilson AM FRCP FRACP FRSA
Dr S. R. Nelson FRCP
Professor Brian Neville
Simon J. Newell MD FRCP FRCPCH
R. C. F. Newton FRCP
Dr Eric Nieman MD FRCP DCH
Dr Brian O'Connell
Dr D. J. O'Donoghue FRCP
Dr S. Oleesky MSc MB(Manchester) MD
    (Washington Univ) FRCP
Dr Janet O'Neill FRCP
Dr P. A. O'Neill MD FRCP
Dr T. E. Oppe CBE FRCP
Dr T. Emlyn Owen FRCP
Dr Stuart Packham MB ChB MRCP(UK)
T. E. Parry MB ChB FRCP FRCPath
Malcolm Parsons FRCP
Dr Vinod Patel MD & Dr Rashni Shukla
    MFPHM
A. D. Paterson FRCP
Alex Paton MD FRCP
J. C. Pease DM FRCP
Richard Peatfield MD FRCP
Professor Brian Pentecost OBE MD FRCP
Sir Denis Pereira Gray OBE PRCGP
Dr M. G. Philpott MD FRCP FRCPCH DCH
Dr Perminder Phull MD MRCP(UK)
Professor C. A. C. Pickering FRCP FFOM
    DIH
Professor Raymond Playford FRCP
Dr Donald Portsmouth FRCP
Surgeon Captain RN P. J. Preston OBE
    FRCP
A. T. Proudfoot FRCP FRCPEdin
Anthony Proust FRCP
Dr Keith Prowse
D. H. H. Pullon FRCP FRCPEdin FRACP
John Puntis FRCP
Angus Rae MB FRCP FRCP(C) FACP
Sir Philip Randle FMedSci FRCP FRS
Dr R. D. Rea
Dr Alan Rees BSc MD FRCP
Dr Philip Rees OBE MA(Cantab)
    MD(Amsterdam) FRCP
Dr Alan Reid FRCP
Professor John Reid
Adrian Reuben FRCP
Dr D. J. Rhodes MB FRCP
Dr John P. Rice FRACP FRCP
Mr Clive Richards OBE
M. R. Richardson FRCP
Dr H. R. C. Riches MD FRCP

Dr Geoffrey H. Robb FRCP
Dr N. R. C. Roberton MA MB FRCP
Dr J. Trevor Roberts FRCP FRCR
Frank Robertson MD FRCP
Dr David Watson Rogers
Professor Richard Rondel FRCP FFPM
Dr J. H. Ross MC MD FRCP
Dr R. P. G. Rothwell FRCP FRACP
Professor Neville Rowell MD FRCP
Peter Rudge
Michael Rudolf FRCP
Dr George Russell FRCP
Dr P. A. Sanders MD FRCP FRCPEdin
Professor G. I. Sandle MD PhD FRCP
Professor Howie Scarffe
Alastair D. Scotland FRCP FRCS FFPHM
C. J. Scott
Professor Sir John Scott KBE MD FRCP
    FRACP FRSNZ
Michael E. Scott MD FRCP FRCPI
Dr D. J. Seddon MA MD FRCP
Professor Y. K. Seedat MD FRCP
Dr K. Shanmugaratnam FRCP
Gavin B. Shaw CBE FRCP FRCPEdin
    FRCPGlasg
W. I. H. Shedden MD FRCP FRCPEdin
C. D. Shee MD FRCP
Dr David I. Shepherd MD FRCP
Jacqueline Sherrard FRCP
Professor N. K. Shinton MD
Dr Roger Shinton MD FRCP
Professor Simon Shorvon FRCP
Dr Paul Siklos FRCP
Dr J. R. Silver FRCP FRCPEdin
Dr Margaret E. Simmons FRCP
Mrs N. E. Singh
Dr Anton Sinniah
Paul W. Skerritt MB BS DPM MRCPsych
    FRCP FRANZCP
P. J. Sleight FRCP
Dr Keith A. Smales MB MRCP(UK)
Dr M. J. Smith MD FRCP
Dr Jane Snell MB BS MRCP(UK)
N. J. C. Snell FRCP FFPM FIBiol
P. J. D. Snow OBE MD FRCP
Dr David Stableforth
Dr Ian Starke MD MSc FRCP
Dr Rosemary Stephens FRCP
James S Stewart MD FRCP
Dr D. J. Stoker FRCP FRCR FRCS
A. R. Stone FRCP FRACP
Dr Richard Stone
Dr W. D. Stone MD FRCP
Anthony Storr FRCP
Dr L. B. J. Stuyt MD FRCP (deceased)
Professor J. A. Summerfield MD FRCP
Dr Geoffrey Summers MB FRCP
D. W. Sumner TD FRCP
Dr C. H. J. Swan MD FRCP
Professor Emeritus William St Clair
    Symmers FRCP FRCPEdin FRCPI
    HonFACP (deceased)
Jean Symons HonMRCP
Dr Prodyot Kumar Talukdar MB BS(Cal)
    FRCP MRCPEdin DCH Eng
Dr Alan Tang FRCP
Professor Martin Tattersall FRCP

R. G. Taylor BSc MD FRCP
Professor Rodney Taylor
Dr G. Terry MB BS(Dunelm) FRCP
Dr Thein Htut MB BS(Rangoon) FRCP
    FRCPEdin FRACP
Dr Adrian Thomas FRCP
Dr Anne L. Thomas PhD MRCP
B. M. Thomas FRCP
Dr P. Thomas FRCP
Professor A. J. Thompson
Paul Thompson MD FRCP
Dr John A. Thomson MD FRCP FRCPGlasg
Dr Graham Thorpe FRCP
G. M. B. Tibbs OBE HonFRCP
Miriam C. Todorovic BA
Dr C. M. Tonks FRCP FRCPsych
Lord Turnberg
Dr M. R. Turner MA MRCP(UK)
Dr Peter P. Turner OBE
Dr A. G. G. Turpie
Dr J. A. Vale FRCP
Professor Jos W. M. Van Der Meer MD
    FRCP
J. Van Gijn MD FRCP
E. M. Vaughan Williams DM DSc FRCP
Dr Tom Venables FRCP FRCGP
Dr Ian Verber FRCP FRCPCH
Professor Julian Verbov MD FRCP FRCPCH
David R. H. Vernon
Dr Katherine Verrier-Jones
Professor O. L. Wade CBE MD FRCP
Dr D. J. Walker
Professor W. F. M. Wallace BSc MD FRCP
    FRCA
Jonathan F. Waller BSc MD FRCP
Professor Michael Walsh
Lord Walton of Detchant FRCP FMedSci
Professor J. D. Ward MD FRCP
Professor O. C. Ward PhD MD FRCP
Dr Simon J. Ward MA MSc MPhil
    MRCP(UK) FRCSEdin
Dr N. Warner MRCP(UK)
Professor Michael D. Warren MD FRCP
    FFPHM
Dr I. M. Waterson MA MB BChir FRCP
    FRCPCH
Dr Sylvia Watkins
Dr D. A. L. Watt FRCP FRCPEdin
    FRCPGlasg
Dr Judith Webb MD FRCP FRCR
Professor A. P. Weetman MD FRCP
Vivian Weinstein FRCP
Clive Weston
John Homer Wetherill FRCP
Professor J. L. Whitby FRCP FRCP(C)
John E. A. Wickham MD MS BSc FRCP
    FRCR FRCS
Dr Nicholas Wickham
Dr I. B. Wilkinson MA BM MRCP(UK)
Owen G. Williams MD FRCP FRCPath
Dr Paul Williams DM FRCP
Tim Williams
Dr Ivor Wilson MB FRCP DHSMA
J. A. C. Wilson FRCP FRCPEdin
John Wilson
Anthony J. Windebank MD FRCP
Dr A. J. Wing DM FRCP

Sir Gordon Wolstenholme
Dr Voi Shim Wong BSc MB ChB MD
  MRCP(UK)
Professor C. B. S. Wood FRCP FRCPCH
Dr J. D. D. Wood FRCP FRCPGlasg
Dr David Woodings FRCP
Dr A. D. Wright
Dr F. W. Wright DM FRCP FRCR
James Wright FRCP
Peter Wright FRCP FRCS FRCOphth
Dr Stephen J Wroe MD FRCP
A. L. Wyman MD FRCP
Dr Tim Wynne-Williams FRCP
Dr Bryan Youl MD FRCP
Dr Giles Youngs MD FRCP
Dr Richard Yu
Dr Derek W. Zutshi MB FRCP LLD

INDEX

Illustrations are indicated in italics.